Teacher's Guide

Blue Level

Rose Griffiths

Heinemann Educational Publishers
Halley Court, Jordan Hill, Oxford OX2 8EJ
a division of Reed Educational & Professional Publishing Ltd

Oxford Melbourne Auckland
Florence Prague Madrid Athens
Singapore Tokyo Sao Paulo
Chicago Portsmouth NH (USA) Mexico City
Ibadan Gaborone Johannesburg
Kampala Nairobi Kuala Lumpur

First published 1996

99 98 97 96
10 9 8 7 6 5 4 3 2 1

ISBN 0 435 53327 4

Designed and typeset by Susan Clarke
Illustrated by Tessa Richardson-Jones and Steve Smallman
Cover design by Ron Kamen
Printed and bound in Great Britain by Thomson Litho Ltd.

The author and publishers would like to thank teachers at the following schools for their help in trialling these materials:
Murrayburn Primary School, Edinburgh
St Bernard's RC Primary School, Bristol
Plymouth Grove Primary School, Manchester
Lubenham Primary School, Leicester
St Peters CE Primary School, Leicester
St Peters VE Primary School, Gwent
Cawley Lane Junior School, West Yorkshire
Naphill and Walters Ash Combined School, High Wycombe
Emmer Green Primary School, Reading
St Anne's JMI School, Streetly

Contents

Mathematical content

Overall content for Number Connections

Red level
Counting and place value with numbers to 35
Arithmetic within 15
Mental recall of number bonds to 7

Blue level
Counting and place value with numbers to 75
Arithmetic within 40
Mental recall of number bonds to 10

Green level
Counting and place value with numbers to 120
Arithmetic within 60
Mental recall of number bonds to 15

Yellow level
Counting and place value with numbers to 200
Arithmetic within 100
Mental recall of number bonds to 20

Content of Blue level

Blue Textbook 1

Counting to 50
Grouping in tens
Spelling numbers one to ten
Ordinal numbers: 1st, 2nd, 3rd, 4th
Using money (1p, 2p, 5p, £1 and £10)
Addition and subtraction within 20
Mental recall of number bonds to 8
Multiples of 2, 5 and 10 to 50

Blue Textbook 2

Counting to 60
Grouping in tens
Reading and spelling numbers eleven to twenty
Using money (1p, 5p, 10p, £1, £5 and £10)
Addition and subtraction within 24 (in 1s) and 50 (in 5s and 10s)
Mental recall of number bonds to 9
Multiples of 3 to 18, and of 2, 5 and 10 to 50
Using $\frac{1}{2}$ (half hours on clock)
Ordinal numbers: 1st to 12th

Blue Textbook 3

Counting to 75
Reading and spelling thirty to seventy-five
Using money (1p, 2p, 5p, 10p, 50p, £1)
Addition and subtraction within 40
Mental recall of number bonds to 10
Multiples of 3 to 30; 2 and 5 to 50; 10 to 70
Division (including symbol ÷)

Introduction

Number Connections is an exciting course providing enjoyable and well-structured materials for pupils aged 7 to 11 who have difficulty with mathematics, and in particular with number work. It can be used to support individual, small group or whole-class teaching, depending on how mathematics is organised in the school.

For each of 4 levels, Red, Blue, Green and Yellow, there are three Textbooks, associated Copymasters and a Teacher's Guide.

Stage	**Pupil Books**	**Copymasters**	**Teacher's Guide**
Red			
Blue			
Green			
Yellow			

Using this Teacher's Guide

This guide has been written to be used by class teachers, special needs staff, and any other adults working with the children. As well as these general introductory notes, specific notes for textbook and copymaster pages are included on pages 15 to 62. These explain the **purpose** of each section, list the **materials** needed, and suggest **supporting activities** which can be used as introductory activities before starting the textbook work, or as additional practice later on. The notes on **using the textbook pages** and **using the copymasters** include ideas about how to support children's work, information about any likely difficulties which children may have, and answers for textbook questions. *You may wish to make your own folder of one copy of each copymaster with the answers filled in with red pen.*

Using the pupil materials

The **textbooks** provide attractive, full-colour pages to work from. Children who have had difficulty with mathematics are less likely than others to have used a textbook before, and it is important not to underestimate the help that many children will need, particularly at first, to follow question numbers in the right order and to write their work down in a clear way in an exercise book. You may want to establish a routine – for example, 'title, today's date, question number 1' – so that children know what to do each time they start work. One way of showing how helpful it is to write question numbers and answers clearly, is to ask children to swap books with a friend, then mark their friend's work as you read out the answers.

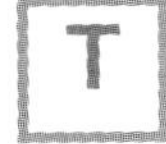

An introduction by the teacher is especially important on pages marked with the icon shown in the margin. Whatever the activity, children will often benefit from an adult reading through each page with them and discussing it, before they start work. Further notes on ways of providing **reading support** are on page 11.

For each pair of textbook pages the **copymasters** provide important additional work in a fill-in format, as well as optional extra practice. The teacher's notes for each copymaster give guidance on this. There are also copymasters with each book to make repeatable games. (See page 10 for a summary of these.) Use the copymasters as flexibly as you wish; you may want children to leave some out, or to repeat some several times. Many copymasters (including the games) provide work suitable for taking home, if wished.

Most of the copymasters are in pairs, and are associated with the same textbook spread. The copymasters can be printed back-to-back, to save paper. (The only exceptions are those which require cutting out.) It is helpful to use a variety of colours of paper if possible, to help differentiate one sheet from another. Avoid dark colours, however, as these reduce legibility.

You may wish to keep a stock of ready-printed sheets for each textbook in a concertina file or an A4 'display book' (which has clear plastic pockets), to avoid the inconvenience of too many trips to the photocopier.

The games can be made most easily if they are printed on card, and will last longer if they are laminated or covered with clear sticky-backed plastic.

Low attainment in number work

Low attainment in mathematics can be due to a great variety of reasons, including absence from school, lack of confidence, low reading ability, poor concentration and memory, and difficulties with understanding abstract ideas. Sometimes children's problems are made worse by the hierarchical nature of some parts of maths: especially with number work, children can fail because they have been moved on to a harder topic before they are sufficiently confident with the easier work on which that topic depends.

Helping children succeed

How can you best help children with number work?

Use a variety of approaches

Because of the varied nature of children's difficulties, they need a variety of teaching approaches. *Number Connections* introduces and practises each topic or skill in several contexts, and children are often encouraged to use two or three complementary methods to solve a problem, to increase their understanding of what they are doing, and to help them memorise important facts. Practical work, discussion, work with a calculator, using equipment, and pencil and paper methods, are all important. Since mental arithmetic is often the most useful method for everyday life, children need to be helped to develop a good repertoire of mental methods, too.

Capitalise on children's own interests and experience

The contexts used in these materials have been chosen both because they are interesting and relevant to children in this age group, and because they can be used to develop children's ability in using and applying maths. It is important to make the most of children's own experience, both in school and at home, so that their number work is purposeful. Many of the activities and games included can be taken home to use with parents or other family members who are keen to help the child make progress.

Use a sensible sequence of work

Each strand of work in these books is revisited several times, each time moving further forward. The sequence of topics and activities within each book (and between books) has been chosen carefully, both to make the most of links between one topic and another, and to provide variety (and hence help children to concentrate, because their interest is held).

To help you to trace the development through a particular number topic, the work is categorised into four strands: Counting and place value (in the early books, including handwriting); Addition and subtraction; Multiplication and division; and Mixed problems. See contents pages, on pages 15, 31 and 47, for work which encompasses elements from the counting and place value, addition and subtraction and multiplication and division strands.

The chart on page iv lists the mathematical content of this level of the scheme.

Encourage children to be independent and responsible

Children who have been unsuccessful at maths in the past sometimes put more effort into avoiding work or copying other people's answers than into trying to understand their work, perhaps because they have convinced themselves they will always fail. Use careful assessment (see Starting points, page 8) to decide the most appropriate starting point for a child, to help them succeed as soon as possible. Encourage them to organise themselves (even though it is often quicker for you to do it for them!) whenever possible, including fetching their own equipment when needed, and putting it away afterwards. A list of useful equipment is included below. Suggest that children work with a friend, so that they can compare answers and explain to each other how they got them.

Equipment

Very little equipment is needed other than the usual classroom stationery – pencils, ruler, scissors, glue and squared and plain paper. You will need:

- *counting equipment* for example, buttons, counters, marbles, craft sticks, centicubes and any other collection of about 70 or 80 items which children would enjoy counting
- *base 10 equipment* such as Multibase or Dienes'
- *bricks* which fit together, for example, Multilink, for counting individually and in groups
- *calculator* with well-spaced buttons and a display which is easy to read. It is helpful if children have the opportunity to use more than one model of calculator
- *coins and notes* – up to 80p in each coin: 1p, 2p, 5p, 10p, 20p, and some 50p and £1 coins. Real coins are better than card or plastic, and should be used at least some of the time. '£5 notes' and '£10 notes' can be made by the children.
- *stopwatch or sand timer* to time tests: 3 minutes, 2 minutes and 1 minute
- *number line* for desk-top or wall, marked 0–50 or more
- *dice* marked 1–6 and 0–5
- *number cards* numbered 0–20 or more.

Some of the supporting activities which are suggested need other inexpensive equipment; this is listed for each activity.

Starting points

Although most children will start work on Red Textbook 1 and then work through the textbooks in order, you can start a child at any point in the scheme. It is better for a child to start on a book which can be completed quickly and successfully, and then move on, than to start on a book which proves too difficult and discourages them. If a child is new to your school or your class, use a combination of methods to decide upon the best starting point:

Previous records Compare the child's records for number work in his or her previous school or class with the list of mathematical content for each textbook on page iv.

Progress tests Ask the child to complete one version of the progress test for each textbook, starting with the easiest, and stopping as soon as the child seems to be finding a test too difficult.

Progress test
Blue Textbook 1 Version A

Name ______
Date ______

1 How many candles? ___

2 Write these numbers as words:
10 8 7

Write the missing numbers:
3 34, 33, 32, 31, ___, ___, ___, ___
4 2 + ☐ = 8
5 7 + 9 = ___
6 22, 24, 26, 28, ___, ___, ___, ___

One spider needs 10 pipecleaners.
7 How many pipecleaners for 5 spiders? ___

8 How much change? £11

9 How much money? ___
10 4 × 5 = ___

64 Teacher's Guide

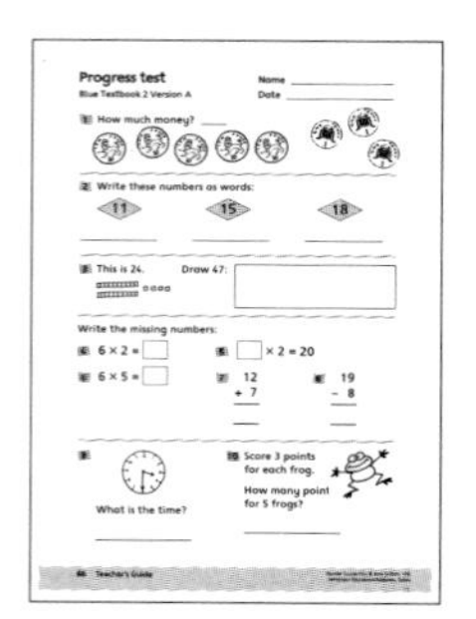

Progress test
Blue Textbook 2 Version A

Name ______
Date ______

1 How much money? ___

2 Write these numbers as words:
11 15 18

3 This is 24. Draw 47:

Write the missing numbers:
4 6 × 2 = ☐
5 ☐ × 2 = 20
6 6 × 5 = ☐
7 12 + 7
8 19 − 8

9 What is the time?
10 Score 3 points for each frog. How many point for 5 frogs?

66 Teacher's Guide

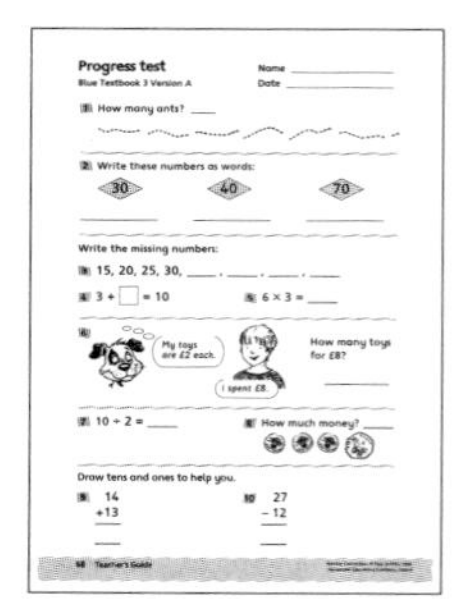

Progress test
Blue Textbook 3 Version A

Name ______
Date ______

1 How many ants? ___

2 Write these numbers as words:
30 40 70

Write the missing numbers:
3 15, 20, 25, 30, ___, ___, ___, ___
4 3 + ☐ = 10
5 6 × 3 = ___

6 My toys are £2 each. I spent £8. How many toys for £8?

7 10 ÷ 2 = ___
8 How much money? ___

Draw tens and ones to help you.
9 14 + 13
10 27 − 12

68 Teacher's Guide

The first activity in each textbook provides a check on whether the child is ready for the work in that book. Follow the advice in the teacher's notes for those pages.

Self-assessment Once a child has made a start on the work in a particular book, discuss with them whether it is at about the right level of difficulty.

Assessment, record keeping and planning

For many mathematical activities, what a child understands and can do is best assessed by observing the child and discussing their work with them. However, pencil and paper tests *are* useful as a way of reminding children about the work they have done, and to demonstrate the progress they have made. Copiable **progress tests** for each textbook are on pages 63 to 69.

Copiable **record sheets** for each textbook are included on pages 70 to 78. There are versions for the teacher and the pupil. The teacher's record covers one textbook and associated copymasters on a single sheet; the pupil's sheets cover half a textbook at a time.

There is space on both the teacher and pupil record sheets to keep notes about other activities, for example those suggested in the supporting activities in the teacher's notes for each page. This space can be used to make a note of any regular practice you would like the child to do, whilst they are working on that book – for example, writing 3 the right way round, or practising counting out money at home once a week.

Individual education plans for children with special needs, specifying each child's particular targets for work in number, are very straightforward to draw up, once you have identified which textbook in *Number Connections* is the most appropriate one for the pupil. Use the statements of mathematical content listed on the chart on page iv. (The list is also repeated at the top of the teacher's record sheet for each book.)

Curriculum coverage

See pages 79 and 80 for curriculum information for England and Wales, Scotland and Northern Ireland.

Games

Games provide useful extra practice for children who are trying to develop fluency with numbers and mental recall of number facts. It is helpful if an adult can play each new game once or twice with the child, to make sure they understand what to do; thereafter, children can use the illustrated instructions as a reminder if needed.

Most games can be played by 1, 2 or 3 people. Many children will find it helpful to practise on their own for a while, as well as playing with others.

The games included in the textbooks, and those made from copymasters, can be used as often as you wish, starting from the point where they are introduced. Extra copies of games can be lent to children to take home for additional practice with friends and family.

Textbook 1

Sums which make 8 (pages 14 and 15 onwards; B26, B27 and B28)
Number bonds to 8.

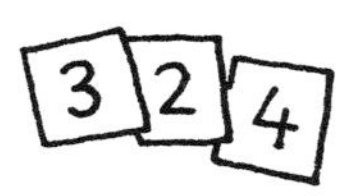

Fifty pence (pages 24 and 25 onwards; B29 and B30)
Counting in 5s up to 50.

Red and black (page 31)
Addition within 20.

Textbook 2

Sixty pence (pages 4 and 5 onwards; B56 and B57)
Counting in tens and ones up to 60.

Tens and ones (pages 8 and 9 onwards; B58 and B59)
Seeing what happens when you add 10 or 1.

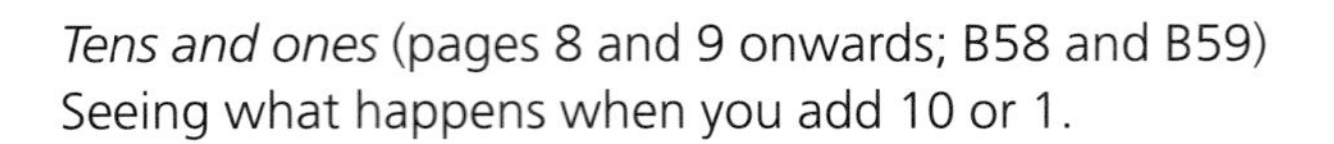

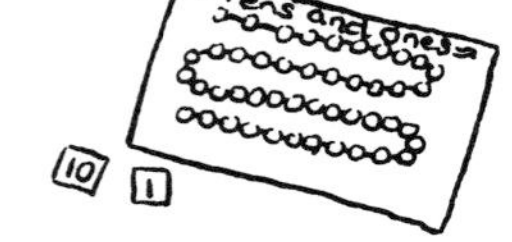

Make 9 (pages 14 and 15 onwards; B60 and B61)
Number bonds to 9.

Textbook 3

Tens and teens bingo (pages 6 and 7 onwards; B88 and B89)
Practising saying, listening to and reading numbers which are hard to distinguish (e.g. 13 and 30).

Sums which make 10 (from pages 10 and 11 onwards; B90, B91 and B92)
Number bonds to 10.

Reading support

Many children who have difficulties with number work find reading difficult as well. Teaching reading can often go hand-in-hand with teaching maths, and using non-fiction texts as well as fiction increases the opportunities to repeat important words and phrases. Children who have been relatively unsuccessful when reading stories may be more confident with the *Number Connections* books, because of the high level of repetition, the help provided by illustrations, and the activity involved.

Liaison

The approach to teaching reading which is most effective will vary from one child to another. Liaison between the child's usual teacher for maths, and their teacher for reading (if it is not the same person) is important.

Motivation

One of the most important factors in whether a child will be successful when reading a text is their motivation. Discussion before a child starts work (which will include saying out loud many of the words they will soon read) is very helpful. The contexts for number work in these books have been chosen because they are of interest to many children, and a few minutes talking with a child to make personal links with their own experience is time well spent.

Key words and phrases

Most of the vocabulary used in *Number Connections* will be familiar to children; but sometimes they will be introduced to new words and phrases which are important in maths.

These **key words and phrases** are used frequently:

how many	count	you need
draw	answers	make
write	ask your teacher	use
take turns	copy and complete	fill in the missing numbers
check	add	take away
altogether	find as many ways as you can	

There are copiable **word lists** for the Blue textbooks on the next three pages. Each list gives twelve words, firstly in the order they are introduced in that book, and then in alphabetical order with an illustration for each word. All the words can be learnt in context in the textbooks.

These are some ways of using the lists for additional practice:

- Give each child a copy of the word list to keep in their copymaster folder. Ask them to colour in each picture when they first come across the word in the textbook.
- Talk to the child about learning to read some new words over the next few weeks. Ask the child to read the list of words at the top of the page (ie without illustrations). Circle any words they already know well. Repeat this every now and then, as the child works through the textbook, and circle new words learnt. Suggest that children work with a partner if they want to, and test each other.
- Make a set of word cards from the list (by printing onto card if possible). Cut out each of the 12 rectangles, and write the word for each card on the back of the illustrated card. Children can practise with these by trying to read the word without the picture, then turning over to see if they are right.

Word list

Name ____________________

Blue Textbook 1

box leg bat heart spider pipecleaners stopwatch
sand timer t-shirt skittles coins playing cards

bat

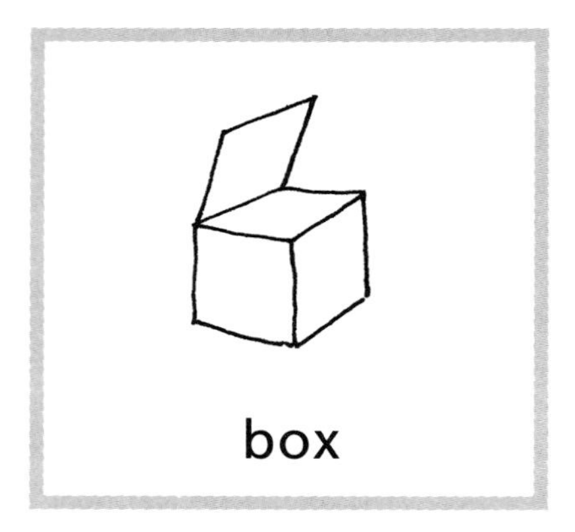
box

coins

heart

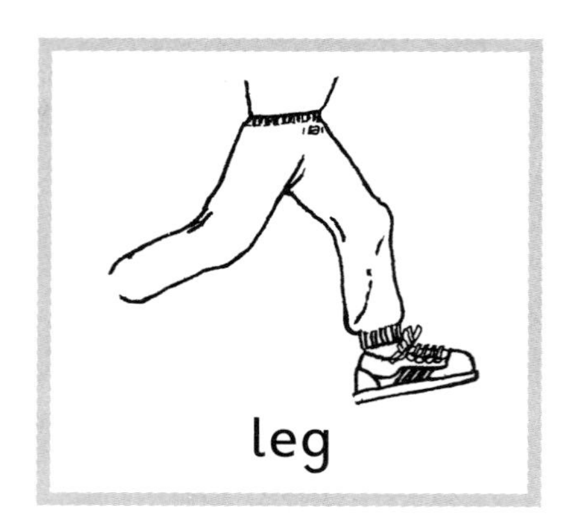
leg

pipecleaners

playing cards

sand timer

skittles

spider

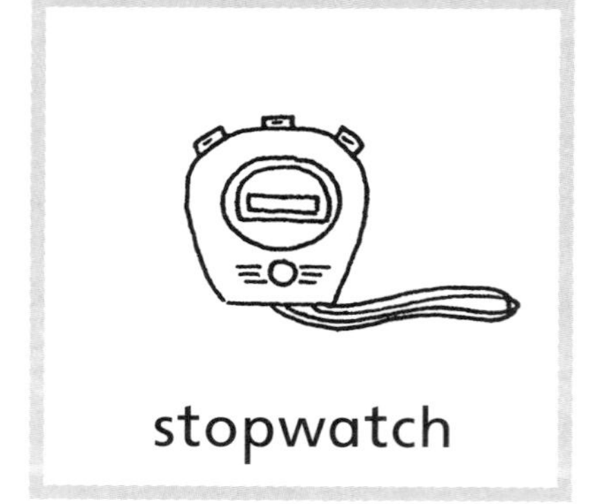
stopwatch

t-shirt

Word list

Name ______________________

Blue Textbook 2

pennies ten pence bird clock hand red
yellow blue number line score starfish photo

bird

clock

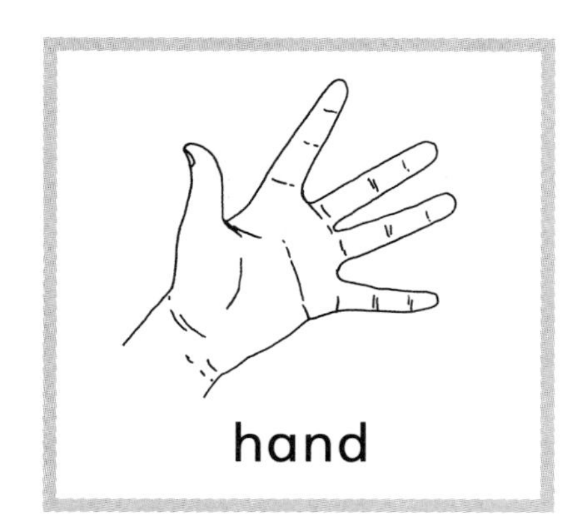
hand

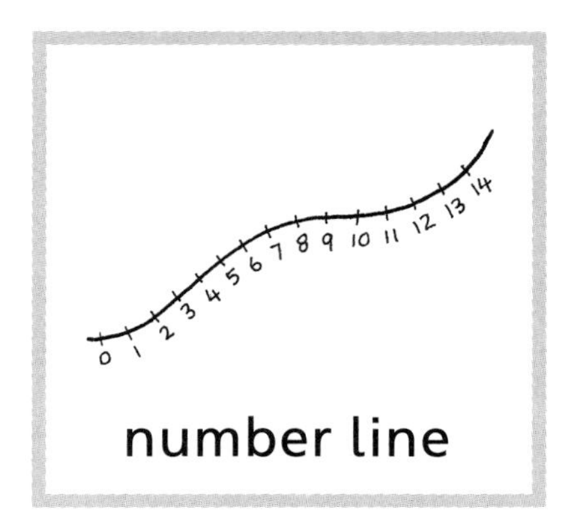

number line

ten pence

pennies

photo

score

starfish

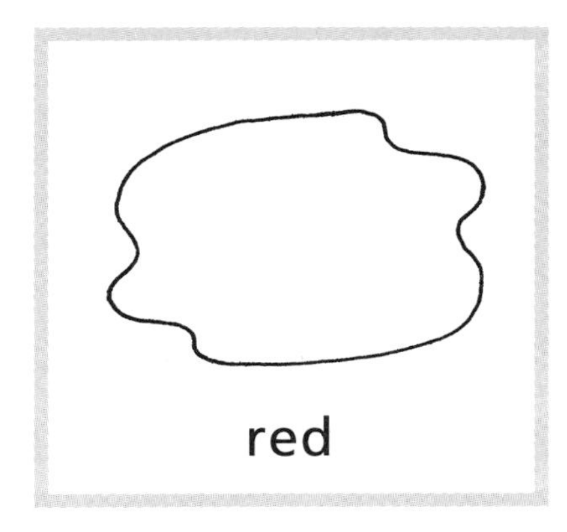
red

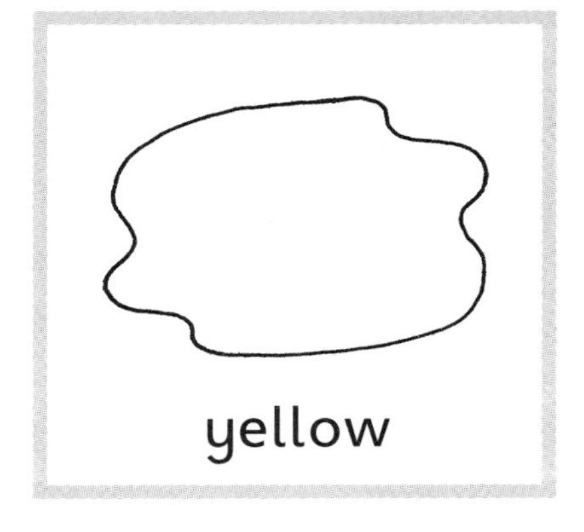
yellow

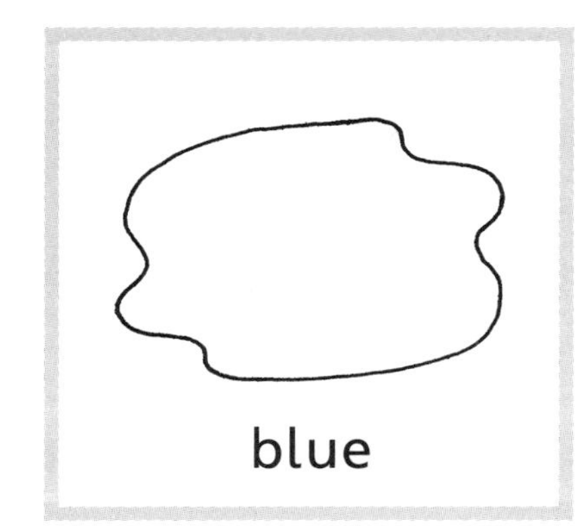
blue

Word list

Name ______________________

Blue Textbook 3

biscuit ant eyeball four fourteen forty
football adult junior locker tin dozen

adult

ant

biscuit

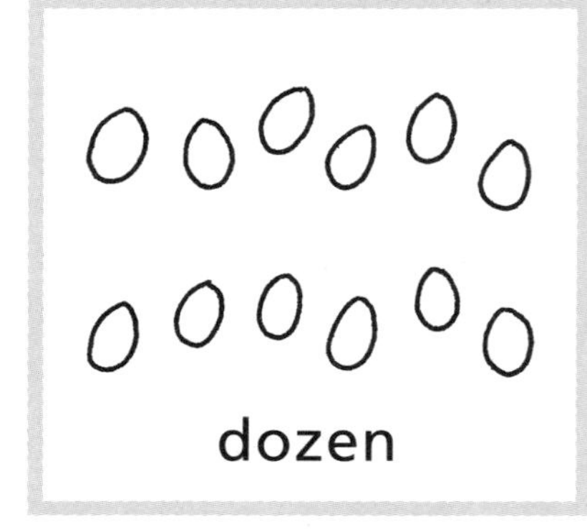

dozen

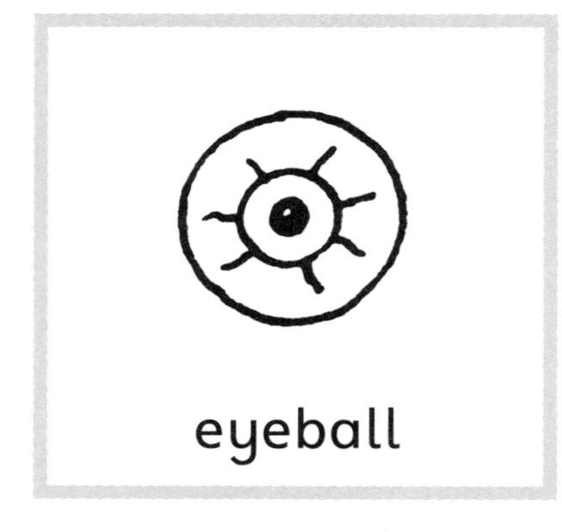

eyeball

football

forty

four

fourteen

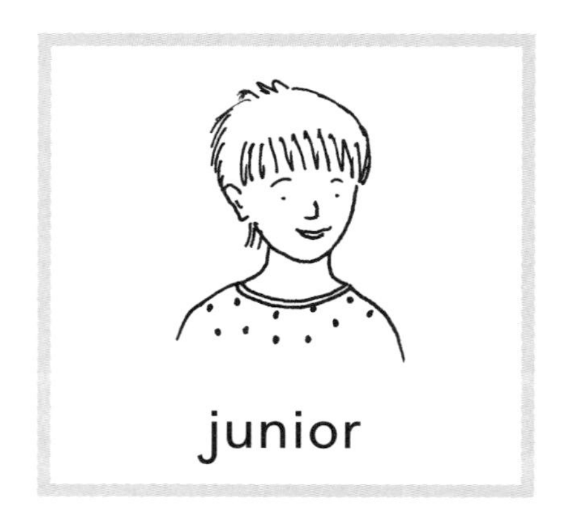

junior

locker

tin

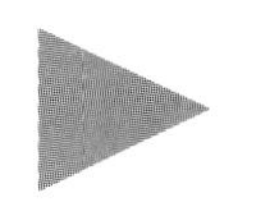

Blue Textbook 1 / Copymasters B1–B30

Contents

■ (grey) Counting and place value

■ Addition and subtraction

● Multiplication and division

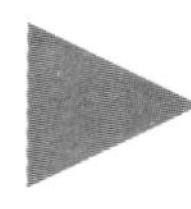

Textbook 1 pages 4 and 5

Fill the box

Textbook pages 4 and 5

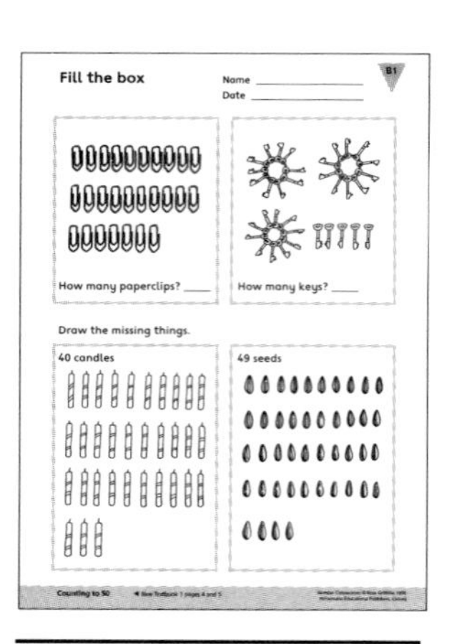

Copymaster B1

Purpose

Practising counting numbers of objects, up to 50

Materials

Polydron, Clixi or similar construction equipment, to make a box
Collection of up to 50 small objects (see question 6)
Paperclips, cake candles, unwanted keys, sunflower seeds (optional: for supporting activity)

Supporting activities

- Use 50 paperclips, candles, keys or seeds. (See Copymaster Bl.) Count them singly, then count them by putting them in tens first. Which is easier?

Using the textbook pages

Counting objects on a picture is more difficult than counting real things, because you cannot move things out of the way as you count them. The objects shown on textbook page 5 are arranged in rows to make counting easier. Encourage children to point to each item as they count it. Demonstrate that you can check your counting by counting again in a different order.

Watch how children answer question 5, to assess their counting. Children who are confident and accurate when counting to 50 will probably count, 'Ten, twenty, thirty, one, two, three, four: thirty four' Those who are less confident (and therefore need more practical practice) are more likely to count, 'One, two, three, four, five …' and so on, to thirty four. 'Pick up bricks' on textbook pages 26 and 27 provides more practice at grouping in tens.

(NB Any child who has difficulty counting the 34 items should be given further practical work to increase their skill at counting up to 35 objects, *before* continuing with work in this book. Red Textbook 3 includes activities and games which will help.)

Question 6 may be done as a predominantly practical question, just writing down the number of items collected, or the child may wish, for example, to draw their ten favourite items collected.

Answers **1** 10 **2** 10 **3** 10 **4** 4 **5** 34 **6** Child's own number of items

Using the copymaster

Copymaster B1 Colouring in the candles and seeds helps many children count them more easily; many children will count as they colour, then count again when they have finished colouring and drawing.

Textbook 1 pages 6 and 7

More or less

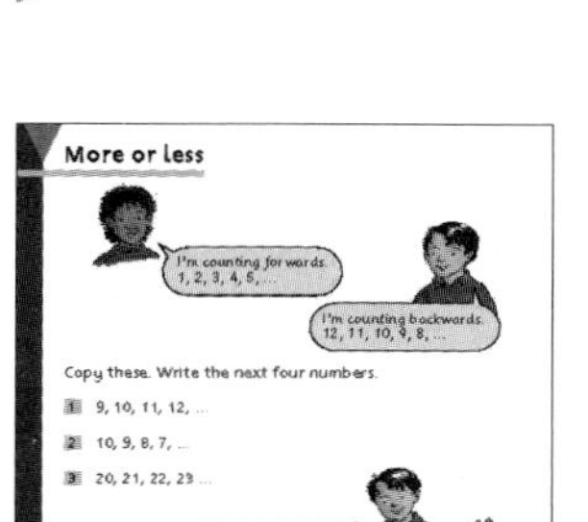

More or less

Copy these. Write the next four numbers.

1 9, 10, 11, 12, ...
2 10, 9, 8, 7, ...
3 20, 21, 22, 23 ...
4 15, 14, 13, 12, ...
5 23, 24, 25, 26, ...
6 30, 29, 28, 27, ...
7 23, 22, 21, 20 ...
8 17, 16, 15, 14, ...
9 35, 36, 37, 38, ...
10 38, 39, 40, 41, ...

Counting backwards or forwards to 50

11 What is one more than 13?
12 What is one more than 19?
13 What is one more than 37?
14 What is one more than 48?
15 What is one less than 16?
16 What is one less than 34?

Counting backwards or forwards to 50

Textbook pages 6 and 7

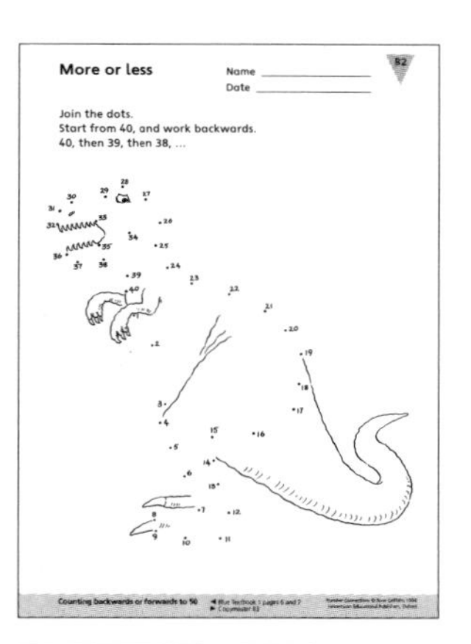

More or less Name ______ Date ______ B2

Join the dots.
Start from 40, and work backwards.
40, then 39, then 38, ...

Counting backwards or forwards to 50

More or less Name ______ Date ______ B3

Fill in the missing numbers.

1	2	3	4			7		9	10
11	12			15	16		18		
	22	23	24				28		30
31		33		35		37		39	
	42		44		46		48		50

What is one less than 20? ____
What is one less than 30? ____
What is one less than 40? ____
What is one less than 50? ____

Counting backwards or forwards to 50

Copymasters B2 and B3

Purpose

Practising saying and writing numbers to 50 in order
Practising counting backwards
Understanding 'more than' and 'less than'

Materials

Desk-top or wall number line marked at least to 50 (optional: for supporting activity)

Supporting activities

- Take turns at counting out loud, forwards or backwards. One person stops, then the other has to carry on counting from there.
- Take turns at asking 'What is one more than ...?' or 'What is one less than ...?', using the number line to help you.

Using the textbook pages

Counting forwards is much easier than counting backwards.

Whichever direction they are counting in, some children may need reassurance when they 'cross the tens', for example, when they count '29, *30*, 31' or '39, *40*, 41'.

If possible, demonstrate *one more than* and *one less than* with actual objects, and on a number line.

Answers **1** 13, 14, 15, 16 **2** 6, 5, 4, **3** 3 24, 25, 26, 27 **4** 11, 10, 9, 8 **5** 27, 28, 29, 30 **6** 26, 25, 24, 23 **7** 19, 18, 17, 16 **8** 13, 12, 11, 10 **9** 39, 40, 41, 42 **10** 42, 43, 44, 45 **11** 14 **12** 20 **13** 38 **14** 49 **15** 15 **16** 33

Using the copymasters

Copymaster B2 Some children may be tempted to join the dots in the usual order, so it is important to explain that everyone needs more practice going backwards, and to check after the first few dots that they are doing this correctly.

Copymaster B3 Additional practice, including completing a number grid. You can also use this sheet to check handwriting for numerals 0 to 9, and for reversed numbers – for example, when a child writes 41 instead of 14. Children whose number formation is poor may benefit from doing some of the activities included in previous textbooks. Red Textbook 2 page 7 included a chart which summarised suggested methods, with a copy for children to keep on Copymaster R34. For particular numbers, children could repeat Copymasters R3 (for numbers 2, 3 and 7), R7 (for 0, 8 and 9), R13 (for 5 and 6) or R21 (for 1 and 4).

Textbook 1 pages 8 and 9

Spelling numbers

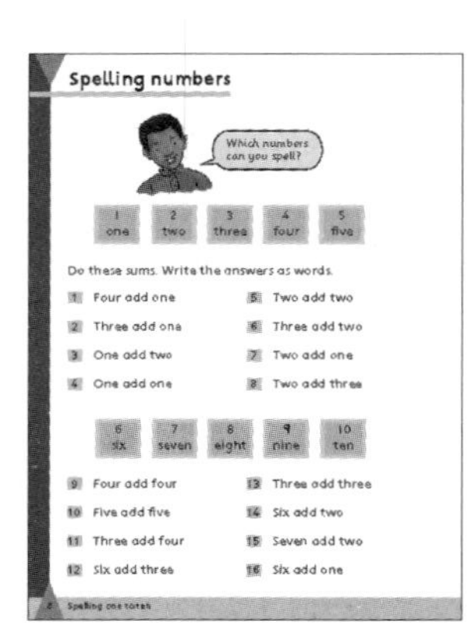

Textbook pages 8 and 9

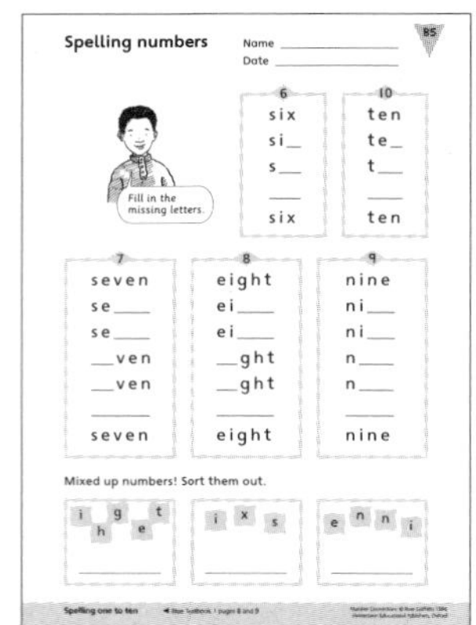

Copymasters B4 and B5

Purpose

Learning and practising the spellings of one to ten
Adding within ten

Materials

1 to 6 dice (optional: for supporting activity)

Supporting activities

- Practise spelling one to six: throw the dice, then write down that number as a word.
- Find out which number has the same number of letters in it as its number. (For example: it is *not* 10, because that has 3 letters: t e n).
- Discuss which words you think are the hardest ones to spell, and why.

Using the textbook pages

Red Textbook 3, pages 6 and 7 'Phone numbers', gave children practice at *reading* the number words from 0 to 9, and many children will be able to spell some of the ten words practised here already. As well as completing the textbook pages and copymasters, children may benefit from further spelling practice. For example, children could work in a pair, testing each other on three or four words at a time and then practising them together.

Answers **1** Five **2** Four **3** Three **4** Two **5** Four **6** Five **7** Three **8** Five **9** Eight **10** Ten **11** Seven **12** Nine **13** Six **14** Eight **15** Nine **16** Seven **17** Eight **18** Four **19** Two **20** Eight **21** Six **22** Four **23** Four **24** Two

Using the copymasters

Copymasters B4 and B5 These provide straightforward spelling practice which concentrates on a different part of each word at a time. The mixed up numbers can be used to focus children's attention on how many letters there are in each word, and on any distinctive letters (for example, the 'w' in 'two').

These sheets can be repeated if needed.

Textbook 1 pages 10 and 11

Eight bats

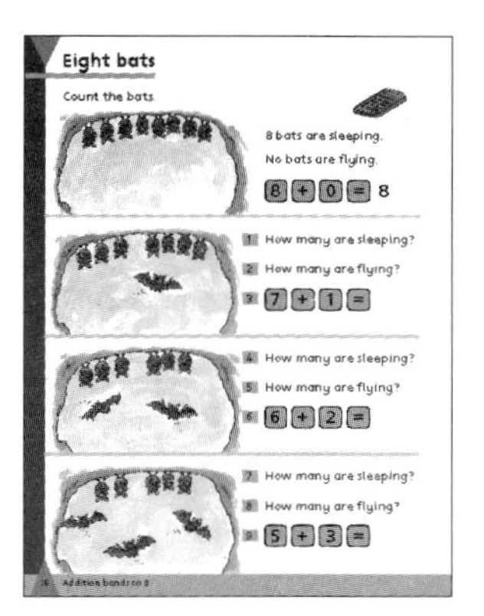

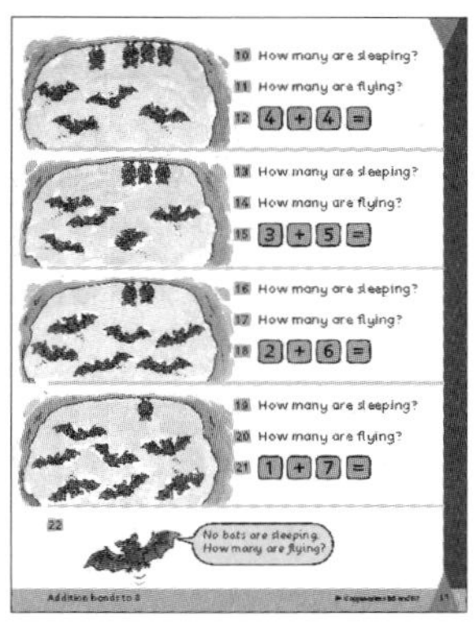

Textbook pages 10 and 11

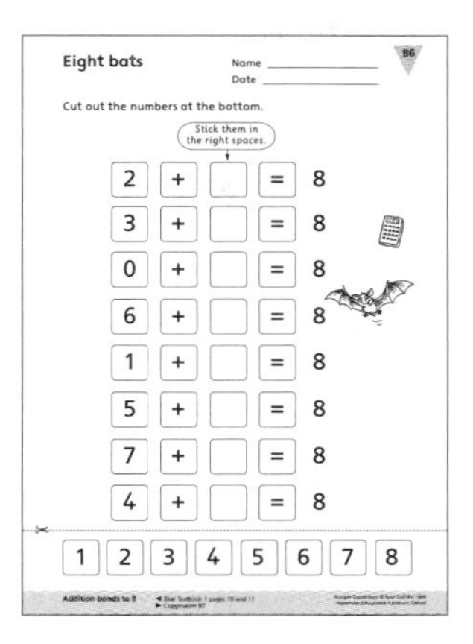

Copymasters B6 and B7

Purpose

Establishing or revising addition bonds which make 8, and improving immediate mental recall of those number facts

Reminding that addition can be done in any order (commutativity)

Materials

Calculator

Scissors and glue (glue stick)

8 small objects (optional: for supporting activity)

Supporting activity

- Put eight counters, small bricks or other small objects on the table in front of you, then hide some with your hand. Your partner has to say as quickly as possible how many are hidden. Take turns at this.

Using the textbook pages

These pages follow a similar pattern to 'Turtle sums' on pages 10 and 11 in Red Textbook 3, which looked at addition bonds to 7, so most children should be confident about what to do here.

Check that children *do* count the bats *and* use the calculator to get the answers, as this repetition will help them memorise the number facts. Point out the pairs of facts – for example, 3 + 5 and 5 + 3 both add up to 8.

Answers **1** 7 **2** 1 **3** 8 **4** 6 **5** 2 **6** 8 **7** 5 **8** 3 **9** 8 **10** 4 **11** 4 **12** 8 **13** 3 **14** 5 **15** 8 **16** 2 **17** 6 **18** 8 **19** 1 **20** 7 **21** 8 **22** 8

Using the copymasters

Copymaster B6 The cut-out numbers enable children to experiment to find the missing numbers if they are not already certain which is which; they should check each sum with a calculator before they glue the number down.

Copymaster B7 A child who is confident with these number bonds can use this sheet as a test. Children who still need support can use the octopus's eight arms (or bats!) to help them; they should also check each answer as they go along, to help them memorise them.

The 'pairs' of facts are emphasised in the boxes at the bottom of the sheet.

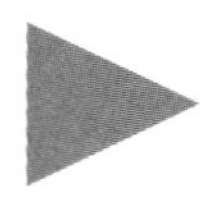

Textbook 1 pages 12 and 13

Number links

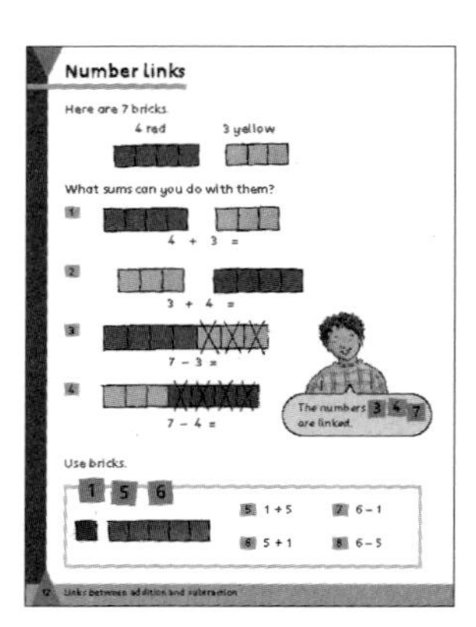

Number links

Here are 7 bricks.
4 red 3 yellow

What sums can you do with them?

1 4 + 3 =
2 3 + 4 =
3 7 − 3 =
4 7 − 4 =

The numbers 3 4 7 are linked.

Use bricks. 1 5 6

5 1 + 5
6 5 + 1
7 6 − 1
8 6 − 5

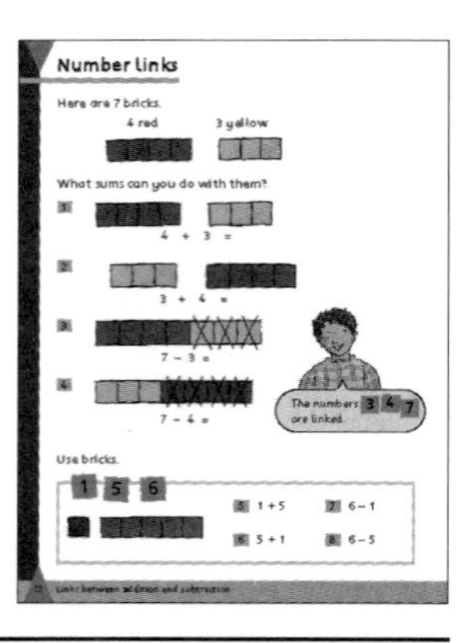

Number links

Here are 7 bricks.
4 red 3 yellow

What sums can you do with them?

4 + 3 =
3 + 4 =
7 − 3 =
7 − 4 =

The numbers 3 4 7 are linked.

Use bricks.

1 + 5
5 + 1
6 − 1
6 − 5

Textbook pages 12 and 13

Number links Name Date B8

Use bricks to do these.

1 6 7: 1 + 6 = __ 6 + 1 = __ 7 − 1 = __ 7 − 6 = __

2 6 8: 2 + 6 = __ 6 + 2 = __ 8 − 2 = __ 8 − 6 = __

3 5 8: 3 + 5 = __ 5 + 3 = __ 8 − 3 = __ 8 − 5 = __

1 4 5: 1 + 4 = __ 4 + 1 = __ 5 − 1 = __ 5 − 4 = __

Make up 4 sums with these: 2 4 6

__ + __ = __
__ + __ = __
__ − __ = __
__ − __ = __

Links between addition and subtraction

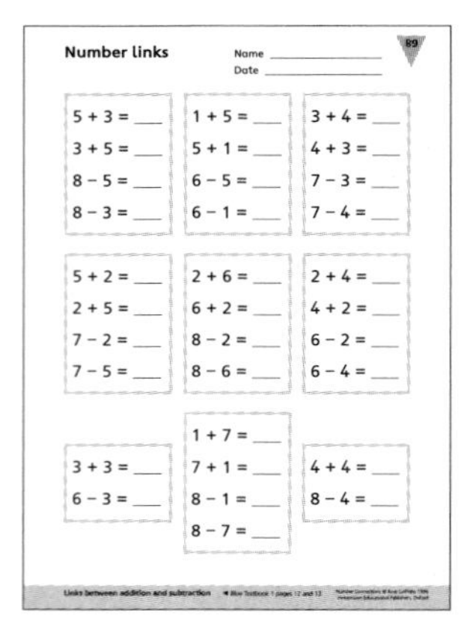

Number links Name Date B9

5 + 3 = __	1 + 5 = __	3 + 4 = __
3 + 5 = __	5 + 1 = __	4 + 3 = __
8 − 5 = __	6 − 5 = __	7 − 3 = __
8 − 3 = __	6 − 1 = __	7 − 4 = __
5 + 2 = __	2 + 6 = __	2 + 4 = __
2 + 5 = __	6 + 2 = __	4 + 2 = __
7 − 2 = __	8 − 2 = __	6 − 2 = __
7 − 5 = __	8 − 6 = __	6 − 4 = __
3 + 3 = __	1 + 7 = __	4 + 4 = __
6 − 3 = __	7 + 1 = __	8 − 4 = __
	8 − 1 = __	
	8 − 7 = __	

Links between addition and subtraction

Copymasters B8 and B9

Purpose

Demonstrating the links between addition and subtraction
Establishing or revising addition and subtraction bonds within 8, and improving mental recall of those number facts

Materials

Multilink or similar bricks which fit together
Cards numbered 1 to 8 (optional: for supporting activity)

Supporting activity

- Shuffle the cards. Turn over the top three cards. Are they linked, like the ones in the textbook? (i.e. can you add two of them to make the third one?) If not, put them at the bottom of the pile and start again. If there is a link, write down the addition and subtraction sums you can make with the three numbers.

Using the textbook pages

It is important that children use bricks to show each example on the textbook pages, as this will help them memorise these number facts. It also demonstrates very clearly how the numbers are linked. It is not always self-evident to children that if two smaller numbers are added together, and you then take one of them away, the other one must be left.

The work done here on number bonds within 8 is followed up in 'Off by heart' on textbook pages 14 and 15, and in 'Speedy sums' on textbook pages 18 and 19.

Answers **1** 4+3=7 **2** 3+4=7 **3** 7–3=4 **4** 7–4=3 **5** 1+5=6 **6** 5+1=6 **7** 6–l=5 **8** 6–5=1 **9** 2+5=7 **10** 5+2=7 **11** 7–2=5 **12** 7–5=2 **13** 3+2=5 **14** 2+3=5 **15** 5–3=2 **16** 5–2=3 **17** 3+3=6 **18** 6–3=3 **19** 4+4=8 **20** 8–4=4

Using the copymasters

Copymaster B8 Encourage children to use bricks to demonstrate why these sums work, both for the groups of sums with an illustration and for those without. The addition bonds have all been practised for mental recall before (see 'Eight bats' on textbook pages 10 and 11), but the subtraction facts are likely to be less familiar.

Copymaster B9 A child who feels confident with these number bonds can use this sheet as a test. Children who are less confident should be encouraged to use bricks.

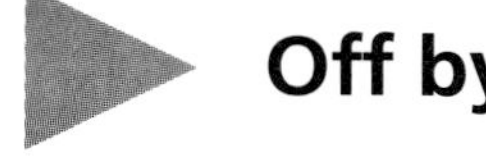

Textbook 1 pages 14 and 15

Off by heart

Off by heart

If you do a sum lots of times, you can learn the answer off by heart.

1 2 + 1 =
2 1 + 3 =
3 0 + 5 =
4 3 + 0 =
5 1 + 2 =
6 4 + 0 =
7 2 + 2 =
8 3 + 1 =
9 2 + 3 =
10 4 + 1 =
11 1 + 4 =
12 3 + 2 =

Now try with bigger numbers.

13 1 + 5 =
14 2 + 4 =
15 5 + 1 =
16 4 + 2 =
17 3 + 3 =
18 6 + 1 =
19 1 + 6 =
20 3 + 4 =
21 4 + 3 =
22 2 + 5 =
23 6 + 0 =
24 5 + 2 =

25 5 + 2
26 4 + 3
27 2 + 6
28 3 + 4
29 4 + 1
30 6 + 1

31 4 + 4
32 3 + 5
33 2 + 6
34 8 + 0

Mental recall of addition within 8

Textbook pages 14 and 15

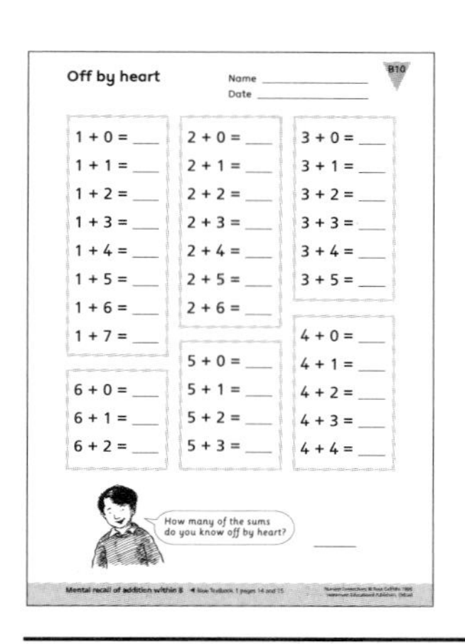

Off by heart B10

Name ____
Date ____

1 + 0 = ___
1 + 1 = ___
1 + 2 = ___
1 + 3 = ___
1 + 4 = ___
1 + 5 = ___
1 + 6 = ___
1 + 7 = ___

2 + 0 = ___
2 + 1 = ___
2 + 2 = ___
2 + 3 = ___
2 + 4 = ___
2 + 5 = ___
2 + 6 = ___

3 + 0 = ___
3 + 1 = ___
3 + 2 = ___
3 + 3 = ___
3 + 4 = ___
3 + 5 = ___

6 + 0 = ___
6 + 1 = ___
6 + 2 = ___

5 + 0 = ___
5 + 1 = ___
5 + 2 = ___
5 + 3 = ___

4 + 0 = ___
4 + 1 = ___
4 + 2 = ___
4 + 3 = ___
4 + 4 = ___

Mental recall of addition within 8

Copymasters B10, B26, B27 and B28

Purpose

Checking which sums children already know off by heart
Establishing or revising addition bonds within 8

Materials

Multilink or similar bricks (optional activity with Copymaster B10)

Supporting activity

- ► Play the 'Sums which make 8' game. See Copymasters B26, B27 and B28 below.

Using the textbook pages

These pages aim to consolidate earlier learning of addition bonds within 8, and to make children more aware of which sums they know so well that they no longer need to work them out, because they know the answers 'off by heart'. Textbook page 14 concentrates on sums within 5, and textbook page 15 covers sums within 8.

Answers **1** 3 **2** 4 **3** 5 **4** 3 **5** 3 **6** 4 **7** 4 **8** 4 **9** 5 **10** 5 **11** 5 **12** 5 **13** 6 **14** 6 **15** 6 **16** 6 **17** 6 **18** 7 **19** 7 **20** 7 **21** 7 **22** 7 **23** 6 **24** 7 **25** Yes **26** Yes **27** No **28** Yes **29** No **30** Yes **31** Yes **32** Yes **33** Yes **34** Yes

Using the copymaster

Copymaster B10 This sheet summarises the addition bonds within 8 (with the exception of a few using nought) which children need to learn. The sums are arranged in patterns, so the sheet cannot be used as a test of a child's proficiency (the random arrangements used later on, in 'Speedy sums' on textbook pages 18 and 19, are a better test).

If you wish, children could use two colours of bricks to make the patterns. For example, the sums which start with 4 would look like this:

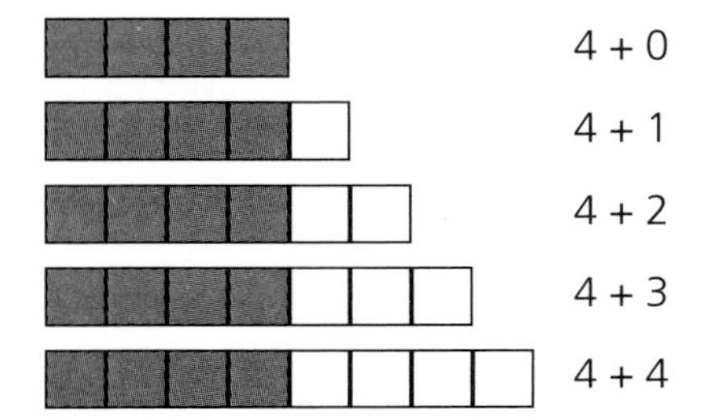

Copymasters B26, B27 and B28 'Sums which make 8' game. This game can be played as many times as you wish, from these pages onwards.

Textbook 1 pages 16 and 17

Spiders and snakes

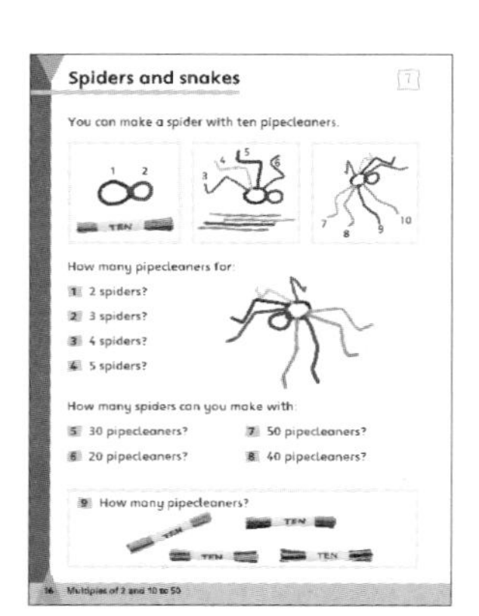

Spiders and snakes 7

You can make a spider with ten pipecleaners.

How many pipecleaners for:

1 2 spiders?
2 3 spiders?
3 4 spiders?
4 5 spiders?

How many spiders can you make with:

5 30 pipecleaners?
6 20 pipecleaners?
7 50 pipecleaners?
8 40 pipecleaners?

9 How many pipecleaners?

16 Multiples of 2 and 10 to 50

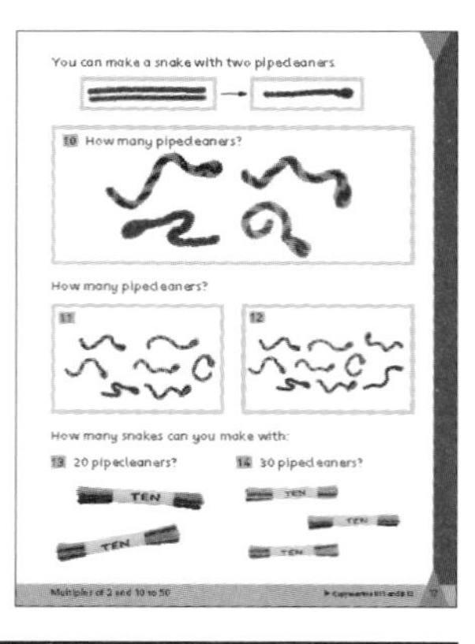

You can make a snake with two pipecleaners.

10 How many pipecleaners?

How many pipecleaners?

11

12

How many snakes can you make with:

13 20 pipecleaners?
14 30 pipecleaners?

Multiples of 2 and 10 to 50

17

Textbook pages 16 and 17

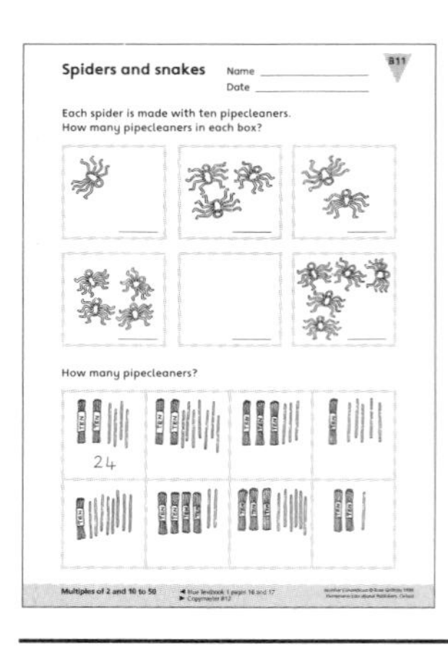

Spiders and snakes Name ______ Date ______ B11

Each spider is made with ten pipecleaners.
How many pipecleaners in each box?

How many pipecleaners?

Multiples of 2 and 10 to 50

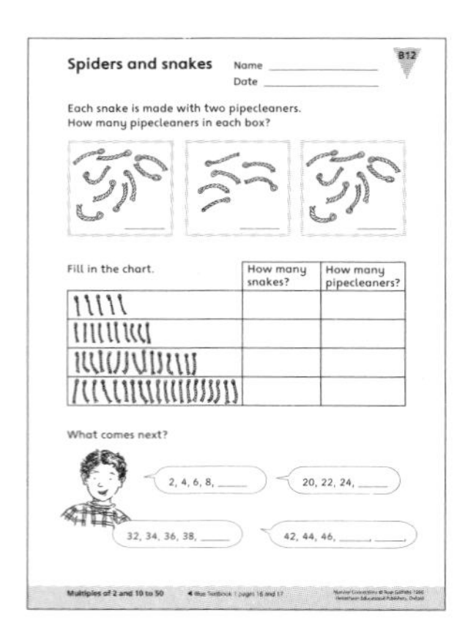

Spiders and snakes Name ______ Date ______ B12

Each snake is made with two pipecleaners.
How many pipecleaners in each box?

Fill in the chart.

	How many snakes?	How many pipecleaners?

What comes next?

Multiples of 2 and 10 to 50

Copymasters B11 and B12

Purpose

Establishing and using multiples of 10 to 50
Establishing and using multiples of 2 to 50
Practising counting in tens and ones

Materials

Pipecleaners in a variety of colours (ideally ten packs of ten)

Supporting activities

- Take turns with a partner. You need 40 pipecleaners in packets of ten, and nine single pipecleaners. Say a number from 10 to 49. Your partner has to give you that many pipecleaners as quickly as possible.
- Work in a group of 2 or 3. Make 25 pipecleaner snakes, like the ones on textbook page 17. Take turns at choosing a number of snakes, and asking 'How many pipecleaners did these need?'

Using the textbook pages

Children who completed Red Textbook 3 practised counting in twos to 34 in 'Frog hops' on pages 22 and 23. They also looked at counting in tens and ones as far as 35, in 'More pounds' on textbook pages 20 and 21. Now counting in twos or tens is extended to 50.

These pages work best if each child is able to make their own spider and snake from pipecleaners, like the ones in the book. Textbook page 16 concentrates on multiples of 10, using them in ways which form the basis of both multiplication (questions 1 to 4) and division (questions 5 to 8). At this stage, children are most likely to solve them by counting; Textbook page 17 uses multiples of 2 in a similar way, with questions 10 to 12 working towards multiplication, and questions 13 and 14 towards division. Question 14 will seem much more difficult than question 13 to some children; remind them that they can use pipecleaners to help answer it.

Work using the multiplication symbol is introduced later in this book, in 'Bat and fives' on textbook pages 28 and 29. The division symbol is left until Blue Textbook 3, and is used first in 'Dog's toys', on textbook pages 22 and 23.

Answers **1** 20 **2** 30 **3** 40 **4** 50 **5** 3 **6** 2 **7** 5 **8** 4 **9** 40 **10** 8 **11** 14 **12** 18 **13** 10 **14** 15

Using the copymasters

Copymaster B11 Point out that if there are no spiders, then no pipecleaners were used.

Copymaster B12 Check the first line of answers in the chart before children continue.

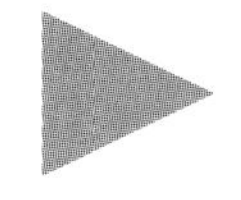

Textbook 1 pages 18 and 19

Speedy sums

Speedy sums

Use a stopwatch or a sand timer.

Can you get 10 sums right in 3 minutes?

1	2 + 4 =	6	1 + 4 =
2	1 + 7 =	7	3 + 3 =
3	5 + 3 =	8	6 + 2 =
4	4 + 0 =	9	4 + 3 =
5	2 + 2 =	10	0 + 3 =

Check your answers. ✓ or ✗

How many of these sums can you get right in 3 minutes?

1	7 − 2 =	6	3 − 1 =
2	4 − 1 =	7	4 − 3 =
3	8 − 4 =	8	2 − 2 =
4	5 − 3 =	9	7 − 4 =
5	6 − 5 =	10	6 − 2 =

✓ or ✗

Mental recall of bonds within 8

How many can you get right in 3 minutes?

1	4 + 2 =	6	5 − 1 =
2	6 − 4 =	7	3 + 5 =
3	7 + 0 =	8	7 − 3 =
4	4 − 2 =	9	6 + 1 =
5	1 + 5 =	10	3 − 3 =

Can you get 20 sums right in 3 minutes?

Check your answers. ✓ or ✗
Count how many you got right.

Talk to your teacher about what to do next.

Mental recall of bonds within 8

Textbook pages 18 and 19

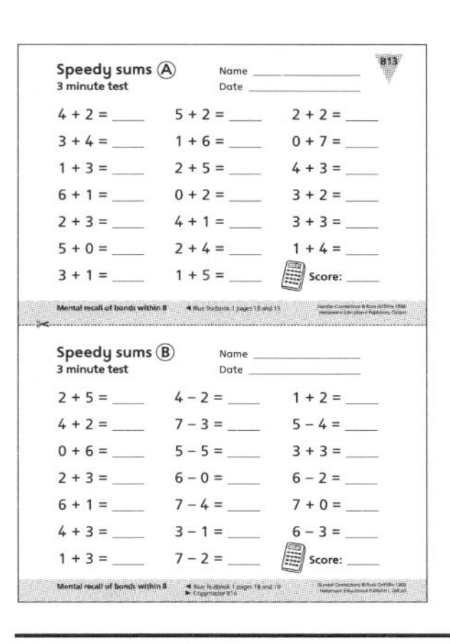

B13

Speedy sums Ⓐ Name ________
3 minute test Date ________

4 + 2 = ___	5 + 2 = ___	2 + 2 = ___
3 + 4 = ___	1 + 6 = ___	0 + 7 = ___
1 + 3 = ___	2 + 5 = ___	4 + 3 = ___
6 + 1 = ___	0 + 2 = ___	3 + 2 = ___
2 + 3 = ___	4 + 1 = ___	3 + 3 = ___
5 + 0 = ___	2 + 4 = ___	1 + 4 = ___
3 + 1 = ___	1 + 5 = ___	Score: ___

Mental recall of bonds within 8

Speedy sums Ⓑ Name ________
3 minute test Date ________

2 + 5 = ___	4 − 2 = ___	1 + 2 = ___
4 + 2 = ___	7 − 3 = ___	5 − 4 = ___
0 + 6 = ___	5 − 5 = ___	3 + 3 = ___
2 + 3 = ___	6 − 0 = ___	6 − 2 = ___
6 + 1 = ___	7 − 4 = ___	7 + 0 = ___
4 + 3 = ___	3 − 1 = ___	6 − 3 = ___
1 + 3 = ___	7 − 2 = ___	Score: ___

Mental recall of bonds within 8

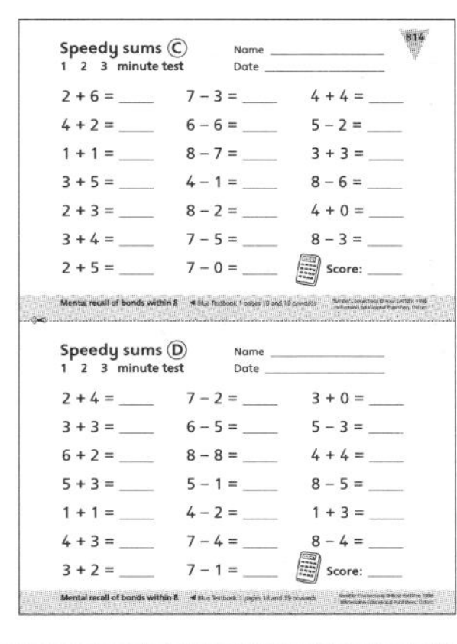

B14

Speedy sums Ⓒ Name ________
1 2 3 minute test Date ________

2 + 6 = ___	7 − 3 = ___	4 + 4 = ___
4 + 2 = ___	6 − 6 = ___	5 − 2 = ___
1 + 1 = ___	8 − 7 = ___	3 + 3 = ___
3 + 5 = ___	4 − 1 = ___	8 − 6 = ___
2 + 3 = ___	8 − 2 = ___	4 + 0 = ___
3 + 4 = ___	7 − 5 = ___	8 − 3 = ___
2 + 5 = ___	7 − 0 = ___	Score: ___

Mental recall of bonds within 8

Speedy sums Ⓓ Name ________
1 2 3 minute test Date ________

2 + 4 = ___	7 − 2 = ___	3 + 0 = ___
3 + 3 = ___	6 − 5 = ___	5 − 3 = ___
6 + 2 = ___	8 − 8 = ___	4 + 4 = ___
5 + 3 = ___	5 − 1 = ___	8 − 5 = ___
1 + 1 = ___	4 − 2 = ___	1 + 3 = ___
4 + 3 = ___	7 − 4 = ___	8 − 4 = ___
3 + 2 = ___	7 − 1 = ___	Score: ___

Mental recall of bonds within 8

Copymasters B13 and B14

Purpose

Establishing or revising addition and subtraction bonds within 8, and improving immediate mental recall of those number facts

Materials

Stopwatch or 3, 2 and 1 minute sand timers (some children may have digital watches with timers on them)
Calculator

Supporting activity

- Play the 'Sums which make 8' game, made from Copymasters B26, B27 and B28.

Using the textbook pages

These pages introduce a series of timed tests which can be used over and over again to improve mental recall of addition and subtraction facts within 8. There are further tests in Blue Textbook 2 pages 18 and 19 (for bonds within 9) and Blue Textbook 3 pages 14 and 15 (for bonds within 10).

Show children how to use a stopwatch or sand timer. Timing can be done by the teacher, or two children can take turns in timing each other. Children should mark their own sums with a calculator. This helps them remember any they got wrong; it also shows them that it can be quicker to do smaller sums in your head.

Answers Marked by the children themselves, using a calculator to check

Using the copymasters

Copymaster B13 These two tests are intended as an introduction, to help children practise the routine of completing a test without feeling under too much pressure. 'Speedy sums' test A is addition within 7; test B introduces subtraction as well. Children should fill in their name and the date first, and *then* time the 3 minutes.

Copymaster B14 This provides two parallel tests covering all the significant bonds within 8. Children sitting next to each other can do a test at the same time with one doing test C and one doing test D.

At first, allow children 3 minutes to do as much as they can (and ring the 3 in the top left-hand corner of the test sheet). Repeating the tests, a few days apart, is a good way of helping children learn these off by heart, and their scores usually improve quite quickly. When a child has scored 20 on a test, reduce the time to 2 minutes when they next try it, then finally, if wished, to 1 minute. Children should always be working to beat *their own* previous score, or time – *not* to beat another child. The latter can encourage cheating, and so is not as effective.

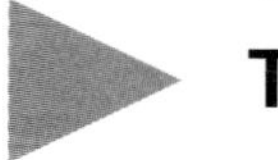

Textbook 1 pages 20 and 21

T-shirts

Textbook pages 20 and 21

Copymasters B15 and B16

Purpose

Using adding on, or subtraction, to calculate change from £10 or £20
Adding up amounts spent, then calculating change from £10 or £20

Materials

Calculator
Colouring pencils (red, yellow and blue)
2 pupil-made '£10 notes' and ten '£1 coins' (optional)

Supporting activity

- Make up some problems like those in the textbook but for buying jeans, jumpers or trainers.

Using the textbook pages

When we use money in real life, we rarely use subtraction to work out the change we should get; the mental method which is probably most common is 'adding on'. When you use a calculator, though, you have to subtract to calculate the amount of change. These pages demonstrate both methods. Children may use any method they wish to answer each question; token notes and coins can be used either to work out the answers or to check them.

If children have difficulty writing the £ sign, they could repeat some or all of the work from Red Textbook 3, pages 18 and 19 'Pounds', with accompanying Copymasters R76 and R77.

Answers **1** £8 **2** £7 **3** £6 **4** £12 **5** £8 **6** £11 **7** £9 **8** £9 **9** £11 **10** Own choice

Using the copymasters

Copymasters B15 and B16 These sheets follow the pattern of textbook pages 20 and 21 respectively, with spaces for children to fill in their own prices. Most will want to continue using prices in whole pounds; a few may like to use prices in pounds and pence, and may consequently need a greater range of token coins to match. They may also want to colour the t-shirts appropriately. After filling in the prices, children then exchange sheets with a friend, and do each other's questions.

Both these sheets can be repeated, if wished.

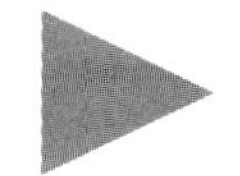

Textbook 1 pages 22 and 23

Bowling

Bowling

We made ten skittles. I put them like this.

From above they looked like this.

I knocked down 8 skittles. That's 2 still standing.

1 I knocked down 3 skittles.
How many still standing?

2 I knocked down 5 skittles.
How many still standing?

3 I knocked down 9 skittles.
How many still standing?

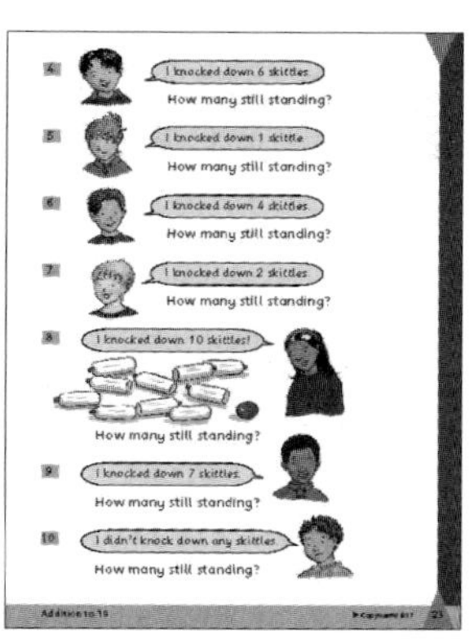

4 I knocked down 6 skittles.
How many still standing?

5 I knocked down 1 skittle.
How many still standing?

6 I knocked down 4 skittles.
How many still standing?

7 I knocked down 2 skittles.
How many still standing?

8 I knocked down 10 skittles!
How many still standing?

9 I knocked down 7 skittles.
How many still standing?

10 I didn't knock down any skittles.
How many still standing?

Textbook pages 22 and 23

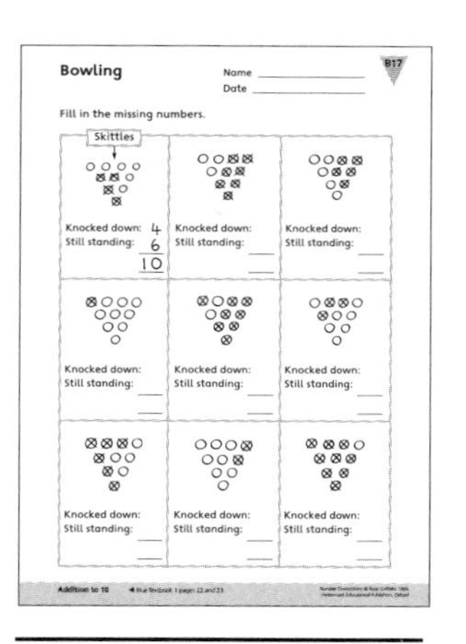

Bowling Name ______ Date ______ B17

Fill in the missing numbers.

Skittles

Knocked down: 4
Still standing: 6
10

Knocked down:
Still standing:

Knocked down:
Still standing:

Knocked down:
Still standing:

Knocked down:
Still standing:

Knocked down:
Still standing:

Knocked down:
Still standing:

Knocked down:
Still standing:

Knocked down:
Still standing:

Addition to 10

Copymaster B17

Purpose

Establishing and practising number bonds to 10
Using a diagram to show a plan view (ie a view from above)

Materials

10 skittles (optional: for supporting activity)

Supporting activities

- ► Play skittles. Each time, count how many skittles are knocked down, and how many are still standing.
- ► Find some other ways of arranging ten skittles. Draw a diagram to show each way you find.

Using the textbook pages

Many children will have played skittles or been ten-pin bowling. Those who have been to a commercial bowling alley may have looked at diagrams on a monitor, showing which pins have been knocked down. If possible, use skittles (or just short pencils!) to make sure children can see why the first diagram on textbook page 22 was drawn as it is.

Pairs of numbers which add to 10 are very important; these number bonds were practised in Red Textbook 3 in 'Make 10' on pages 12 and 13, and they will be returned to in Blue Textbook 3 to be learnt off by heart.

Answers **1** 7 **2** 5 **3** 1 **4** 4 **5** 9 **6** 6 **7** 8 **8** 0 **9** 3 **10** 10

Using the copymaster

Copymaster B17 This sheet revises the addition bonds used in the textbook, presenting them in a vertical instead of a horizontal layout. Children have to use the diagrams to find out what happened in each game.

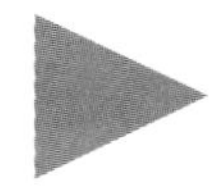

Textbook 1 pages 24 and 25

Fives and ones

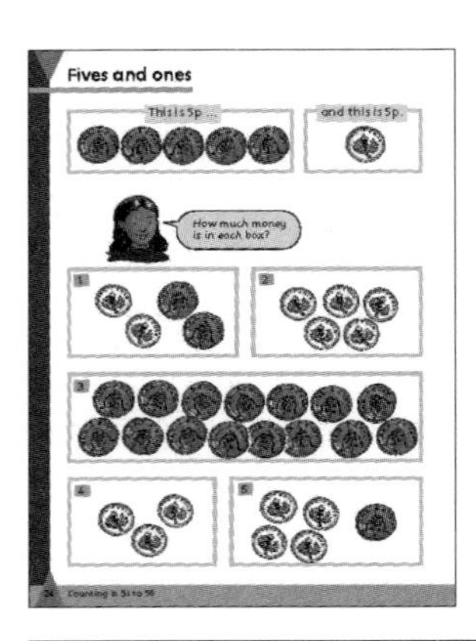

Textbook pages 24 and 25

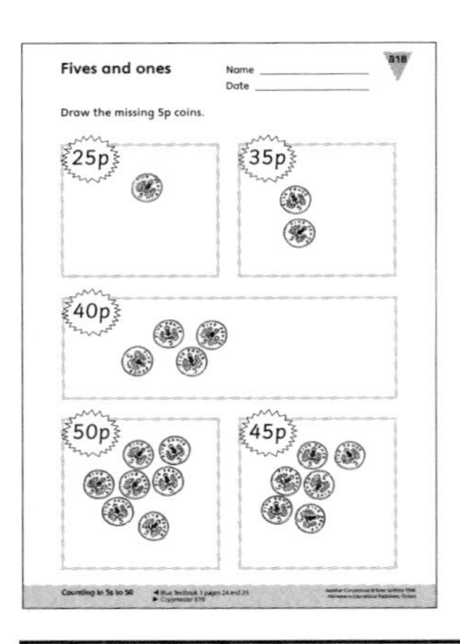

Copymasters B18, B19, B29 and B30

Purpose

Using 5p and 1p coins
Establishing and practising counting in 5s to 50
Counting in 5s and 1s to 50

Materials

50p in 5p coins and 4p in 1p coins (real coins are best, if possible)
(More 1p coins will be needed if children need introductory practice at exchanging five 1p coins for each 5p coin)

Supporting activities

- Practise counting out amounts of money using 5p and 1p coins.
- Play the 'Fifty pence' game. See Copymasters B29 and B30 below.

Using the textbook pages

Most children will know that a 5p coin is worth the same as five 1p coins, but those who are not confident about this will need some initial practice.

Remind children to put 'p' when they write their answers, to show they are working with pence.

Questions 1 to 5 should help children see that using 5p coins can help you count money more quickly than if the amount is entirely in 1p coins.

Questions 6 to 20 help establish which amounts can be made using just 5p coins, and those which need 1p coins as well; this helps distinguish numbers which are multiples of 5 from those which are not.

Answers **1** 12p **2** 25p **3** 15p **4** 15p **5** 21p **6** to **20** Child's drawings or printing

Using the copymasters

Copymaster B18 A straightforward sheet which practises counting in fives.

Copymaster B19 Each sum can be done by counting out the two amounts of money in 5p coins, then counting up how much there is altogether. Children who are confident about counting in fives may not want to use the coins.

Copymasters B29 and B30 'Fifty pence' game. This game practises counting in fives up to 50 (or more). It can be played as many times as you wish, from these pages onwards.

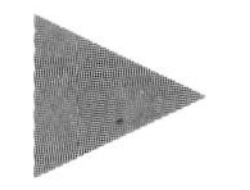

Textbook 1 pages 26 and 27

Pick up bricks

Pick up bricks

Katrina picked up these bricks with one hand.

1 How many bricks?

2 How many bricks?

Grouping in 10s to 50

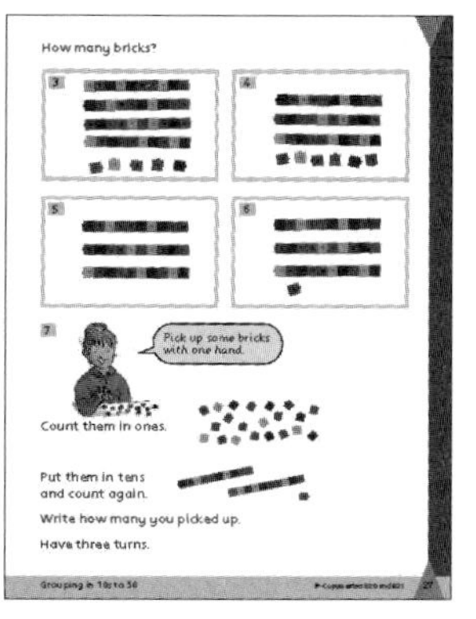

How many bricks?

3

4

5

6

7

Count them in ones.

Put them in tens and count again.

Write how many you picked up.

Have three turns.

Grouping in 10s to 50

Textbook pages 26 and 27

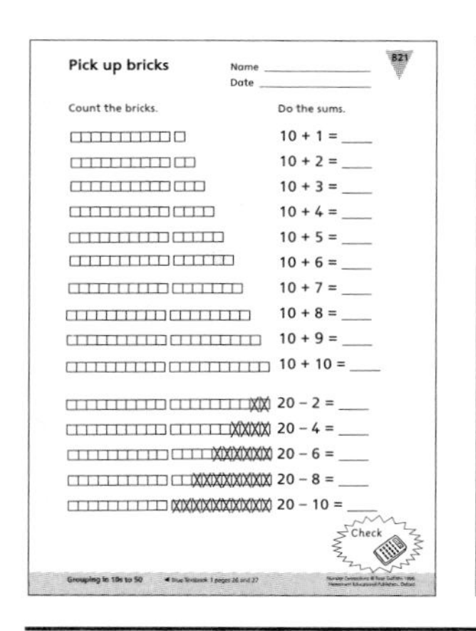

Pick up bricks Name ______ Date ______ B21

Count the bricks. Do the sums.

10 + 1 = ____

10 + 2 = ____

10 + 3 = ____

10 + 4 = ____

10 + 5 = ____

10 + 6 = ____

10 + 7 = ____

10 + 8 = ____

10 + 9 = ____

10 + 10 = ____

20 − 2 = ____

20 − 4 = ____

20 − 6 = ____

20 − 8 = ____

20 − 10 = ____

Check

Grouping in 10s to 50

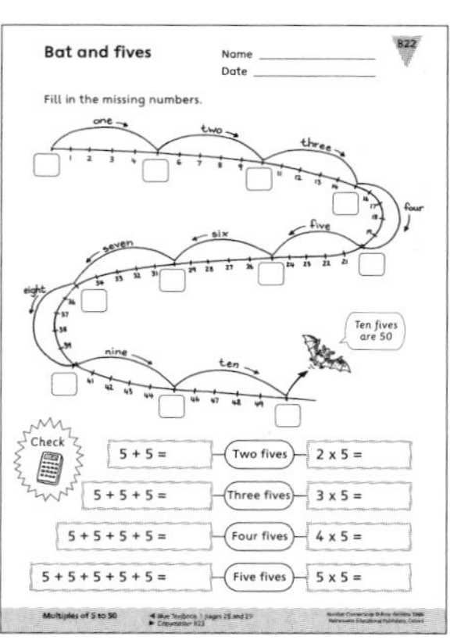

Bat and fives Name ______ Date ______ B22

Fill in the missing numbers.

5 + 5 =	Two fives	2 x 5 =
5 + 5 + 5 =	Three fives	3 x 5 =
5 + 5 + 5 + 5 =	Four fives	4 x 5 =
5 + 5 + 5 + 5 + 5 =	Five fives	5 x 5 =

Multiples of 5 to 50

Copymasters B20 and B21

Purpose

Showing that grouping in tens makes counting quicker and more accurate
Using tens and ones to count, and to add and subtract

Materials

Centicubes or similar centimetre cubes (at least 50)
Calculator

Supporting activity

- ► Practise counting with a partner. Say a number between 10 and 50. Your partner has to give you that many bricks as quickly as possible. Check them, then let your partner choose a number.

Using the textbook pages

These pages continue the work done in 'Fill the box' on textbook pages 4 and 5, but using more abstract equipment. Using cubes which fit together to make tens and ones for counting is a helpful step towards using number equipment such as multibase and Dienes' tens and units. The latter are used from Blue Textbook 2, 'Tens and ones', on pages 8 and 9.

Textbook page 26 concentrates on comparing how quickly and accurately you can count bricks in ones, and those arranged in tens and ones. There are the same number of bricks in each photograph.

Textbook page 27 provides further practice at counting in tens and ones. Question 7 can be done with a friend, to encourage children to talk about the usefulness of grouping in tens to count.

Answers **1** 37 **2** 37 **3** 45 **4** 36 **5** 30 **6** 31 **7** Child's own number

Using the copymasters

Copymaster B20 Check that children can read '1st', '2nd', and '3rd' at the bottom of the sheet.

Copymaster B21 This sheet emphasises numbers 10 to 20, showing how they are made from tens and ones, and helping to build an understanding of place value.

Textbook 1 pages 28 and 29

Bat and fives

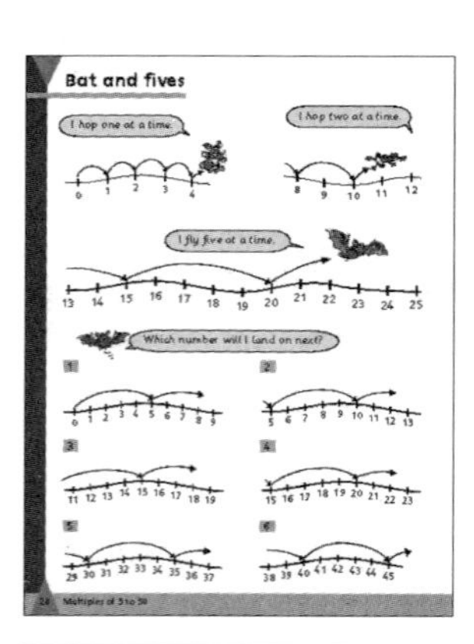

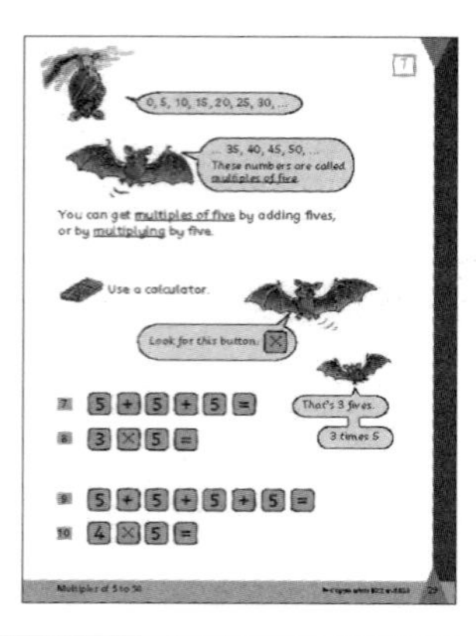

Textbook pages 28 and 29

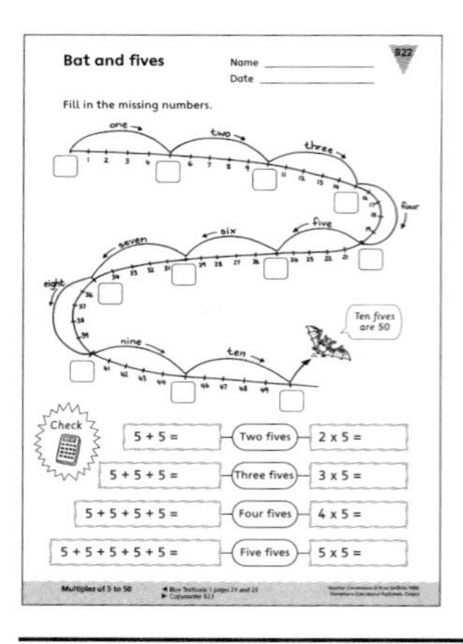

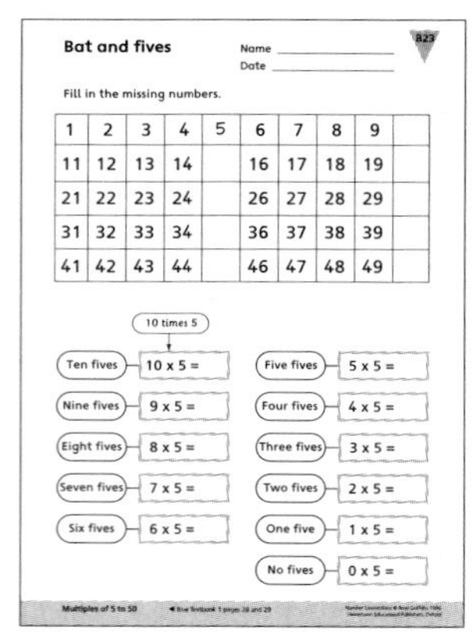

Copymasters B22 and B23

Purpose

Learning the words 'multiples' and 'multiplying'
Using the multiplication symbol, '×'
Using repeated addition to establish multiples of 5 to 50

Materials

Calculator
Desk-top or wall number line to 50 (optional: for supporting activity)

Supporting activity

► Work with a friend. Count forwards on a number line from 0 to 50 in 5s, then back to 0 again. Close your eyes and count forwards and backwards in 5s again, while your friend checks on the number line.

Using the textbook pages

Children have become familiar with the sequence '5, 10, 15, 20, ...' in several places, most recently in 'Fives and ones' on textbook pages 24 and 25. Textbook page 28 follows a similar pattern to 'Rabbit and Frog' in Red Textbook 3 pages 16 and 17, so most children should be able to do questions 1 to 6 quite confidently.

Textbook page 29 takes the important step of introducing the word 'multiples', and explaining that multiples are the result of 'multiplying'. The questions show the link between repeated addition and multiplication, and it is important to make sure that children realise, for example, if we want to add four fives together, that another way of doing so is to calculate 'four times five'. Children need to learn the variety of ways in which we can say '4 × 5', too, and some of these are included on the page.

Using a calculator helps children see the importance of the symbol '×', and helps to make sure they notice the difference between '+' and '×'.

Answers **1** 10 **2** 15 **3** 20 **4** 25 **5** 40 **6** 50 **7** 15 **8** 15 **9** 20 **10** 20

Using the copymasters

Copymaster B22 Discuss the number line on this sheet, to make sure children realise that you can count along the jumps of five to get the answers to the questions at the bottom of the page. For example, going along six lots of five will get you to 30, so 6 × 5 = 30.

Copymaster B23 When children have filled in the missing numbers on the grid, they can colour in the squares with 5, 10, 15, and so on to 50. (Suggest they use a pale colour, so that they can still read the numbers.) Children do further work on multiples of five in Blue Textbook 2, including 'Five times table', on pages 24 and 25.

Textbook 1 pages 30 and 31

Card sums

Textbook pages 30 and 31

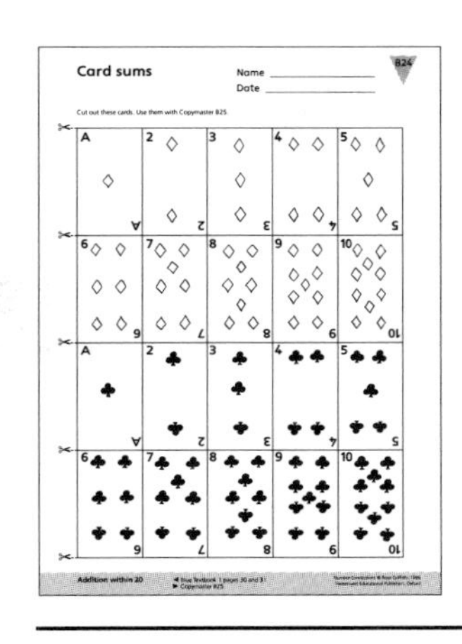

Copymasters B24 and B25

Purpose

Practising addition within 20

Materials

Calculator

A pack of playing cards, without the picture cards (or two copies of Copymaster B24, printed on card)

Scissors and glue (glue stick)

Supporting activity

- ► Use the playing cards. Put them into pairs which add up to 10. How many pairs can you find? Did you have any cards left over?

Using the textbook pages

Most children are familiar with playing cards, and will already know that the 'picture cards' are the jacks, queens, kings and joker (if any), and that the 'ace' is counted as 1. If you are using cards made from Copymaster B24, it is helpful to colour the diamonds red before starting work.

Questions 1 to 6 help introduce the game on textbook page 31. Make sure children get these questions marked before going any further.

The game can be played as many times as you wish, from these pages onwards.

Answers **1** 13 **2** 11 **3** 6 **4** 13 **5** 13 **6** 14

Using the copymasters

Copymaster B24 This can be used to make playing cards, if printed on card, or printed on paper to use with Copymaster B25.

Colouring in the red cards focuses children's attention on the patterns made with different numbers of diamonds.

Copymaster B25 Children should check each pair of cards *before* glueing them down.

This sheet can be repeated if wished.

Textbook 1 page 32

More card sums

More card sums

Work with a friend if you want to.

You need
20 playing cards.

Find as many ways as you can to make 12, with a red card and a black card.

Draw or write down each way.

Addition within 20

Textbook page 32

Purpose

Practising addition within 20
Finding pairs of numbers which add to 12

Materials

20 Playing cards (or cards made from one copy of Copymaster B24)
Calculator

Using the textbook page

This investigation will begin to build children's knowledge of the addition facts which make 12. Most children will approach it in a fairly random manner, looking for any pairs which make 12 and recording them by writing or drawing as they go along. It is best to allow children to use their own methods, rather than trying to impose a more logical approach. You may wish to help children check that they have not repeated a pair.

Altogether, there are 9 possible pairs, leaving just the two aces unused.

This activity can be repeated if wished, using a different number as the 'target' – for example, how many pairs are there which make 15?

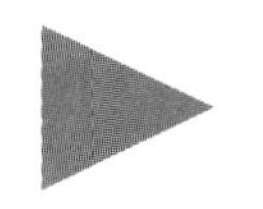

Blue Textbook 2 / Copymasters B31–B61

Contents

■ (grey) Counting and place value

■ Addition and subtraction

● Multiplication and division

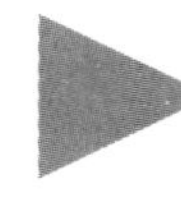

Textbook 2 pages 4 and 5

Coins in a jar

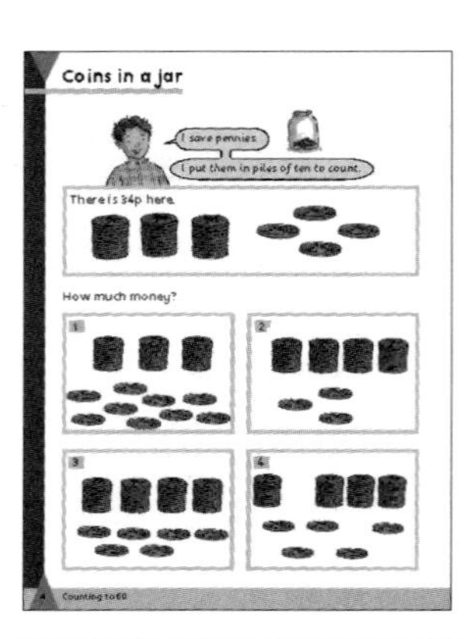

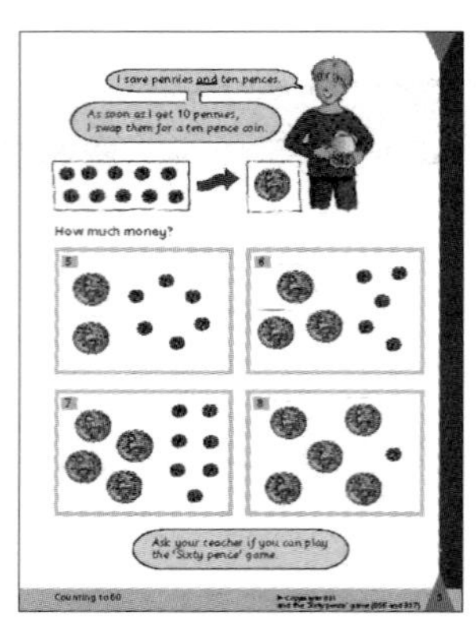

Textbook pages 4 and 5

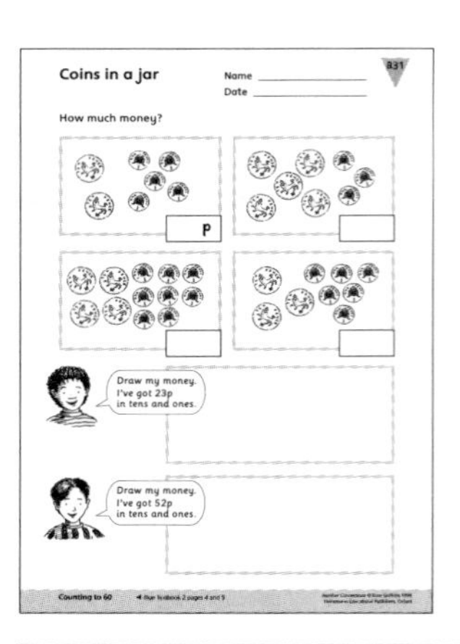

Copymasters B31, B56 and B57

Purpose

Practising counting numbers of objects, up to 60

Materials

60p in pennies – real ones are best (optional: for supporting activities)

Supporting activities

- Use 60p in pennies. Count them one at a time; then count them again, putting them in piles of ten to help you. Which way of counting is easiest?
- Use 60p in pennies. Take turns with a partner to practise counting. Hide some of the pennies in your hand; your partner must count the rest.
- Play the 'Sixty pence' game.

Using the textbook pages

Children will find it helpful to practise counting real pennies by putting them in piles of 10 before starting these pages.

Many children collect pennies, or know someone amongst their families or friends who do so. Further practice at home counting pennies is very useful.

(NB Any child who has difficulty counting the amounts in questions 1 and 2 should be given further practical work, to increase their skill at counting numbers up to 50, *before* continuing with work in this book. Blue Textbook 1 includes activities and games which practise counting up to 50.)

Answers **1** 39p **2** 43p **3** 46p **4** 55p **5** 26p **6** 35p **7** 47p **8** 51p

Using the copymasters

Copymaster B31 Remind children if needed to put 'p' when they write how much money there is.

Copymasters B56 and B57 'Sixty pence' game. This game practises exchanging ten pennies for a ten pence piece, and counting in tens and ones. It can be played as many times as you wish, from these pages onwards.

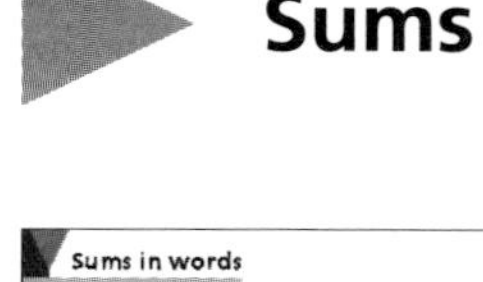

Textbook 2 pages 6 and 7

Sums in words

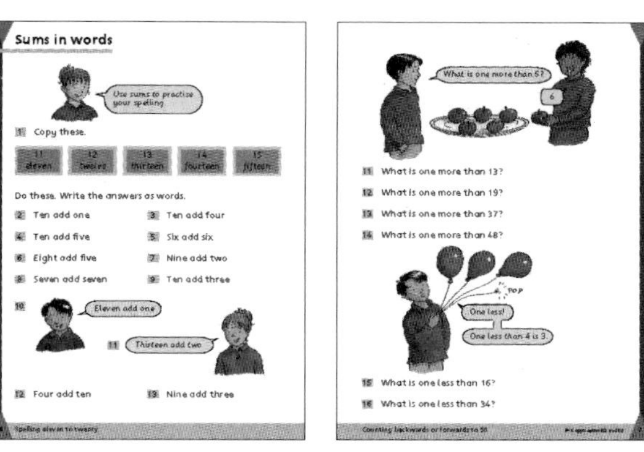

Textbook pages 6 and 7

Copymasters B32 and B33

Purpose

Learning and practising the spellings of eleven to twenty
Addition within twenty

Materials

None

Supporting activities

- Discuss which words you think are the hardest ones to spell, and why.
- Look at the words 'two' and 'twelve'. What do you notice? Why do you think they both start with the same letters?

Using the textbook pages

In Blue Textbook 1 on pages 8 and 9, children practised spelling numbers one to ten. Some children will be able to spell some of the words from eleven to twenty already. As well as completing the textbook pages and copymasters, children may benefit from further spelling practice. For example, they can work in pairs, testing each other on three or four words at a time and then practising them together.

Answers **1** Child's copy of the spellings **2** eleven **3** fourteen **4** fifteen **5** twelve **6** thirteen **7** eleven **8** fourteen **9** thirteen **10** twelve **11** fifteen **12** fourteen **13** twelve **14** Child's copy of the spellings **15** eighteen **16** sixteen **17** twenty **18** nineteen **19** seventeen **20** sixteen **21** nineteen **22** seventeen **23** eighteen **24** twenty

Using the copymasters

Copymasters B32 and B33 These provide straightforward spelling practice which concentrates on a different part of each word at a time. The mixed-up numbers can be used to focus children's attention on how many letters there are in each word, and on any distinctive letters (for example, the 'x' in 'sixteen').

These sheets can be repeated if a child needs more practice.

Textbook 2 pages 8 and 9

Tens and ones

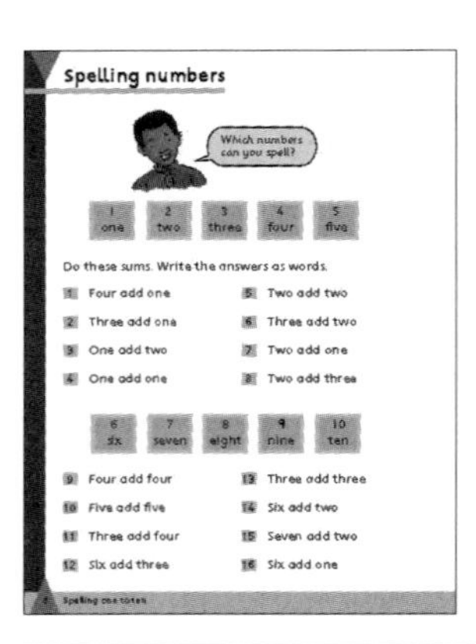
Spelling numbers
Which numbers can you spell?
1 one 2 two 3 three 4 four 5 five
Do these sums. Write the answers as words.
1 Four add one
2 Three add one
3 One add two
4 One add one
5 Two add two
6 Three add two
7 Two add one
8 Two add three
6 six 7 seven 8 eight 9 nine 10 ten
9 Four add four
10 Five add five
11 Three add four
12 Six add three
13 Three add three
14 Six add two
15 Seven add two
16 Six add one

Write the answers as words.
17 How many legs?
18 How many legs?
19 How many legs?
20 How many legs?
21 How many legs?
22 How many legs?
23 How many legs?
24 How many legs?

Textbook pages 8 and 9

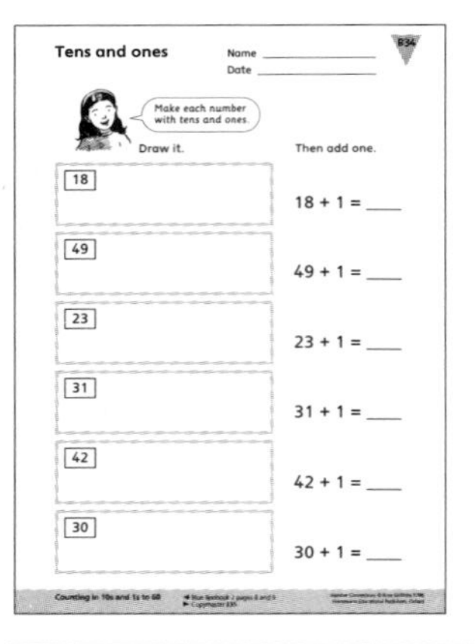
Tens and ones
Name
Date
B34
Make each number with tens and ones.
Draw it.
Then add one.
18 18 + 1 = ___
49 49 + 1 = ___
23 23 + 1 = ___
31 31 + 1 = ___
42 42 + 1 = ___
30 30 + 1 = ___

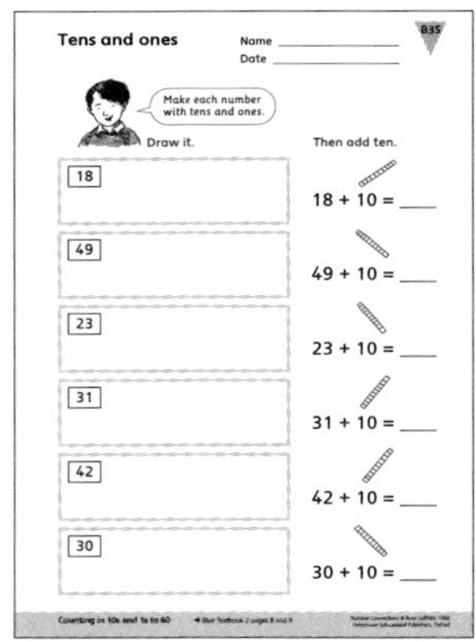
Tens and ones
Name
Date
B35
Make each number with tens and ones.
Draw it.
Then add ten.
18 18 + 10 = ___
49 49 + 10 = ___
23 23 + 10 = ___
31 31 + 10 = ___
42 42 + 10 = ___
30 30 + 10 = ___

Copymasters B34, B35, B58 and B59

Purpose

Showing that grouping in tens makes counting quicker and more accurate
Introducing or revising the use of structured equipment in tens and ones
Seeing what happens to a number when you add one or ten

Materials

Structured equipment in tens and ones (such as Multibase or Dienes')
A set of cards numbered 0 to 60 (optional: for supporting activity)

Supporting activity

► Shuffle a set of cards marked 0 to 60 (or use 0 to 30 at first, then the whole set). Take turns with a friend. Turn over the top card. Make that number with tens and ones, and ask your friend to check it. Then it is your friend's turn.

Using the textbook pages

Structured number equipment in base 10 (ie using ones, tens and, later on, hundreds) is very valuable in extending children's understanding of our number system, and in showing how pencil and paper methods in arithmetic are developed. However, it is important not to underestimate how abstract the equipment can seem. The work done in Blue Textbook 1, in 'Pick up bricks' on pages 26 and 27, where children make their own tens and ones using centicubes, is a helpful step.

Tens which children make themselves sometimes fall apart. Explain that these plastic or wooden tens (which do not come apart) and ones are made to help children learn more about numbers, because counting in tens and ones is so important. Make sure that children can see that a ten is the same length as ten ones put together; show them that they can count to twenty on two tens by counting individual sections.

Textbook page 9 shows children how to draw a number made from base ten equipment. This will be useful not just as a way of showing what they have done with the equipment, but also, later on, as an alternative to using the equipment.

Answers **1** 17 **2** 34 **3** 28 **4** 42 **5** 55 **6** 60 **7** to **18** Child's drawings

Using the copymasters

Copymaster B34 This looks at what happens when you add 1.

Copymaster B35 This looks at what happens when you add 10.

Copymasters B58 and B59 'Tens and ones' game, to practise adding tens or ones. It can be played as many times as you wish, from these pages onwards.

Two times table

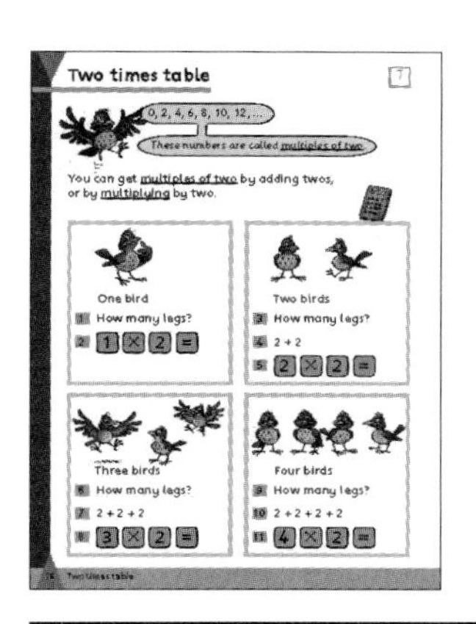
Two times table

0, 2, 4, 6, 8, 10, 12, ...

These numbers are called multiples of two.

You can get multiples of two by adding twos, or by multiplying by two.

One bird
1 How many legs?
2 1 × 2 =

Two birds
3 How many legs?
4 2 + 2
5 2 × 2 =

Three birds
6 How many legs?
7 2 + 2 + 2
8 3 × 2 =

Four birds
9 How many legs?
10 2 + 2 + 2 + 2
11 4 × 2 =

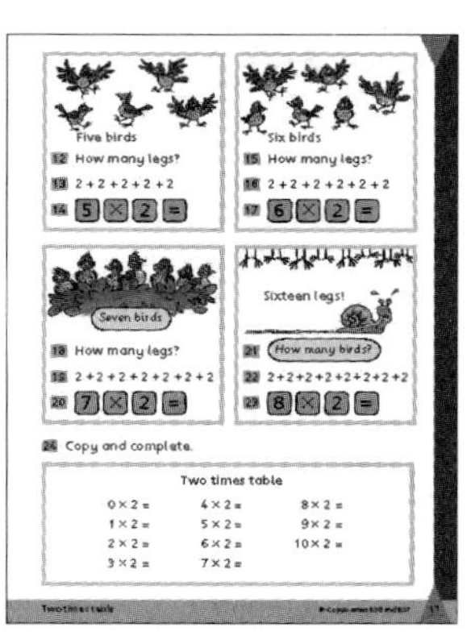
Five birds
12 How many legs?
13 2 + 2 + 2 + 2 + 2
14 5 × 2 =

Six birds
15 How many legs?
16 2 + 2 + 2 + 2 + 2 + 2
17 6 × 2 =

Seven birds
18 How many legs?
19 2 + 2 + 2 + 2 + 2 + 2 + 2
20 7 × 2 =

Sixteen legs!
How many birds?
22 2 + 2 + 2 + 2 + 2 + 2 + 2 + 2
23 8 × 2 =

24 Copy and complete.

Two times table

0 × 2 =
1 × 2 =
2 × 2 =
3 × 2 =
4 × 2 =
5 × 2 =
6 × 2 =
7 × 2 =
8 × 2 =
9 × 2 =
10 × 2 =

Textbook pages 10 and 11

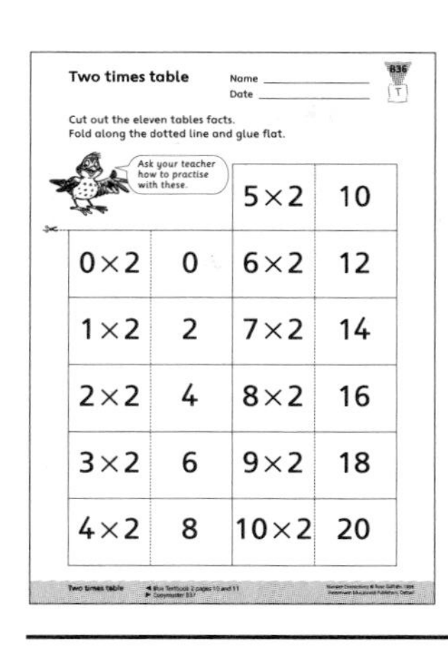
Two times table Name Date B36

Cut out the eleven tables facts.
Fold along the dotted line and glue flat.

Ask your teacher how to practise with these.

		5×2	10
0×2	0	6×2	12
1×2	2	7×2	14
2×2	4	8×2	16
3×2	6	9×2	18
4×2	8	10×2	20

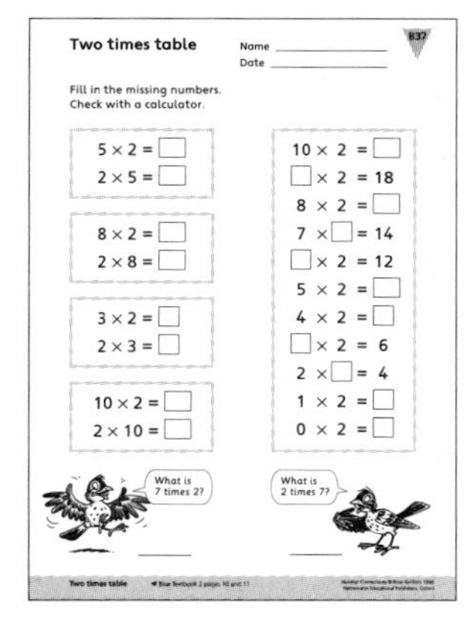
Two times table Name Date B37

Fill in the missing numbers.
Check with a calculator.

5 × 2 = □
2 × 5 = □

8 × 2 = □
2 × 8 = □

3 × 2 = □
2 × 3 = □

10 × 2 = □
2 × 10 = □

10 × 2 = □
□ × 2 = 18
8 × 2 = □
7 × □ = 14
□ × 2 = 12
5 × 2 = □
4 × 2 = □
□ × 2 = 6
2 × □ = 4
1 × 2 = □
0 × 2 = □

What is 7 times 2?

What is 2 times 7?

Copymasters B36 and B37

Purpose

Establishing and beginning to learn the 2 times table facts
Practising the words 'multiples' and 'multiplying'

Materials

Calculator
Scissors and glue (glue stick)
Envelope (to keep tables cards in)

Supporting activities

- Practise counting from 0 to 20 in twos out loud, then back from 20 to 0.
- Use the cards made from Copymaster B36 to practise the two times table.

Using the textbook pages

Questions 1 to 20 emphasise each table fact through a picture (on which children can count the legs), by adding 2 over and over again, and by using a calculator to multiply. Make sure children realise that, for example, adding 5 lots of 2 together gives you the same answer as working out 5 ¥ 2.

Question 21 poses a multiplication problem 'back to front' (and an adult would solve this, intuitively, by dividing: the inverse of multiplication). It is important that children gradually become confident with their tables facts in any order, and that they can answer both sorts of question: 'What is two times ...?' *and* 'How many twos make ...?' It is also important to include learning $0 \times 2 = 0$. Check that children agree that if there are no birds, then there are no legs!

Answers **1** 2 **2** 2 **3** 4 **4** 4 **5** 4 **6** 6 **7** 6 **8** 6 **9** 8 **10** 8 **11** 8 **12** 10 **13** 10 **14** 10 **15** 12 **16** 12 **17** 12 **18** 14 **19** 14 **20** 14 **21** 8 **22** 16 **23** 16 **24** Copy of the two times table

Using the copymasters

Copymaster B36 This sheet makes eleven small cards, with a tables question on one side and the answer on the other. Show children how to practise; shuffle the cards, and put them in a pile, questions upwards. Answer the question, then turn over to see if you got it right. If you did, put it to one side; if not, put it at the bottom of the pile to try again. Then use the cards the other way up – look at the answer, and say what the question is. Use the cards as frequently as you wish; children can work individually, or with a partner, or take them home to practise.

Copymaster B37 Children who are confident can use this sheet as a test. Those who still need support should check each fact with a calculator as they go along.

Textbook 2 pages 12 and 13

Hours and half hours

Textbook pages 12 and 13

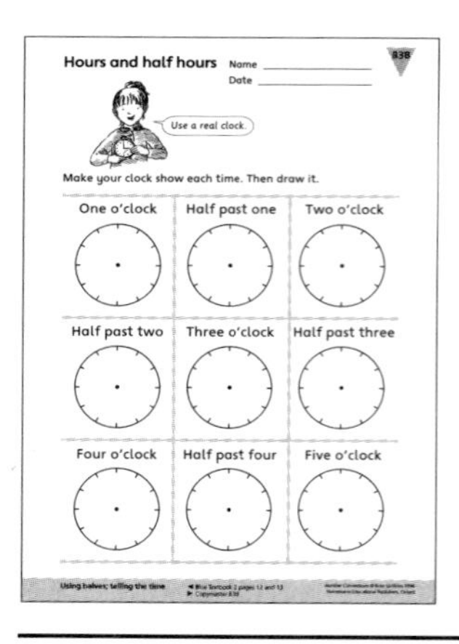

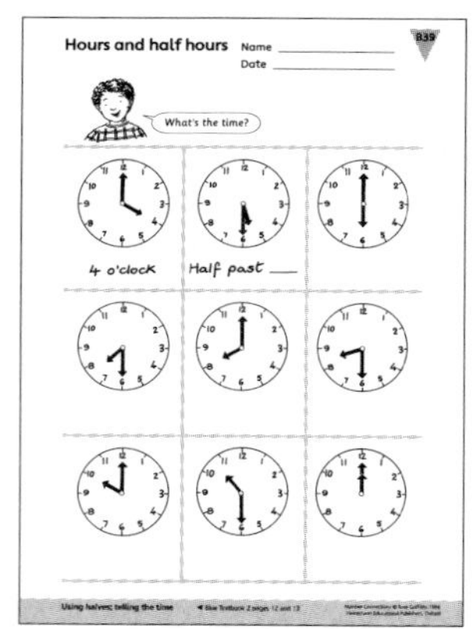

Copymasters B38 and B39

Purpose

Using halves in an everyday context
Looking at the position of the hour hand on a clock
Telling the time on the hour and half-hour

Materials

A working analogue (ie not digital) clock
A clock face with just the hour hand (made by pupil or teacher if wished)

Supporting activity

- During a whole school day, write down what you were doing at every 'o'clock' and 'half-past' time.

Using the textbook pages

Before starting work on these pages, it helps many children to turn the hands on a real clock, starting at 1 o'clock and pausing at each o'clock time back to 1 o'clock again. Make sure children realise that the direction the hands travel is called 'clockwise'.

Talk to children about the fact that a long time ago (before there were railways and factories), clocks only had hour hands, because people did not need to be able to tell the time very accurately. Use a classroom-made clock face with just an hour hand if you wish, to reinforce the work done on these two textbook pages.

When children do questions 13 and 14, using a real clock, if they concentrate on getting the hour hand pointing to exactly the right place, the minute hand will automatically point to 12 and then 6.

Answers **1** No **2** Yes **3** No **4** 5 o'clock **5** 8 o'clock **6** 11 o'clock **7** Half past 5 **8** 6 o'clock **9** Half past 7 **10** Half past 9 **11** 10 o'clock **12** Half past 11 **13** and **14** Child's own drawings

Using the copymasters

Copymaster B38 Copying from a real clock helps ensure that children draw the hour hand in the right position for the half-hour times.

Copymaster B39 Straightforward practice at telling the time.

Textbook 2 pages 14 and 15

Nine counters

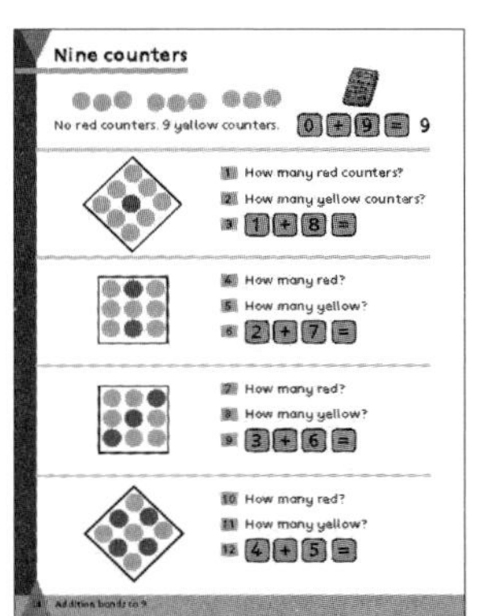
Nine counters

No red counters. 9 yellow counters. 0 + 9 = 9

1 How many red counters?
2 How many yellow counters?
3 1 + 8 =

4 How many red?
5 How many yellow?
6 2 + 7 =

7 How many red?
8 How many yellow?
9 3 + 6 =

10 How many red?
11 How many yellow?
12 4 + 5 =

13 How many red counters?
14 How many yellow counters?
15 5 + 4 =

16 How many red?
17 How many yellow?
18 6 + 3 =

19 How many red?
20 How many yellow?
21 7 + 2 =

22 How many red?
23 How many yellow?
24 8 + 1 =

Textbook pages 14 and 15

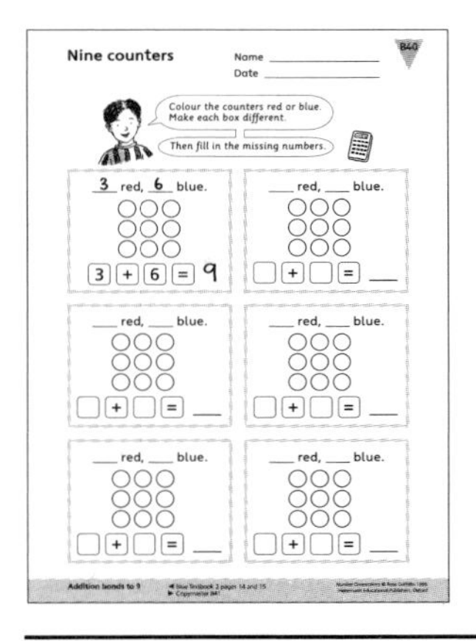
Nine counters Name Date B40

3 red, 6 blue. 3 + 6 = 9

___ red, ___ blue.

Nine counters Name Date B41

2 + □ = 9
4 + □ = 9
6 + □ = 9
3 + □ = 9
8 + □ = 9
5 + □ = 9
1 + □ = 9
7 + □ = 9

□ + 0 = 9
□ + 5 = 9
□ + 3 = 9
□ + 6 = 9
□ + 2 = 9
□ + 4 = 9
□ + 8 = 9
□ + 7 = 9

4 + □ = 9
□ + 4 = 9

5 + □ = 9
□ + 5 = 9

6 + □ = 9
□ + 6 = 9

3 + □ = 9
□ + 3 = 9

Copymasters B40, B41, B60 and B61

Purpose

Establishing and practising addition bonds which make 9, and improving immediate mental recall of those number facts

Materials

Calculator
9 counters (optional: for supporting activity)

Supporting activity

► Put nine counters on the table in front of you, then hide some with your hand. Your partner has to say as quickly as possible how many are hidden. Take turns at this.

Using the textbook pages

These pages follow a similar pattern to 'Eight bats' on pages 10 and 11 in Blue Textbook 1, which looked at addition bonds to 8, so most children should be confident about what to do here.

Check that children count the counters *and* use the calculator to get the answers, as this repetition will help them memorise the number facts. Point out the pairs of facts – for example, 4 + 5 and 5 + 4 both add up to 9.

Answers **1** 1 **2** 8 **3** 9 **4** 2 **5** 7 **6** 9 **7** 3 **8** 6 **9** 9 **10** 4 **11** 5 **12** 9 **13** 5 **14** 4 **15** 9 **16** 6 **17** 3 **18** 9 **19** 7 **20** 2 **21** 9 **22** 8 **23** 1 **24** 9

Using the copymasters

Copymaster B40 If wished, children can work in pairs; each child colours the six lots of counters, then gives their sheet to a friend for them to fill in the matching numbers.

Copymaster B41 Children who feel confident with number bonds to 9 can use this sheet as a test. Those who still need help can use the drawing of nine counters at the top of the sheet.

Copymasters B60 and B61 'Make 9' game. This is similar to the game called 'Make 5' on Copymasters R31 and R32. It can be played as many times as you wish, from these pages onwards.

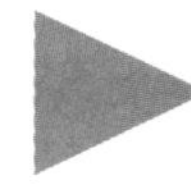

Textbook 2 pages 16 and 17

Fives and tens

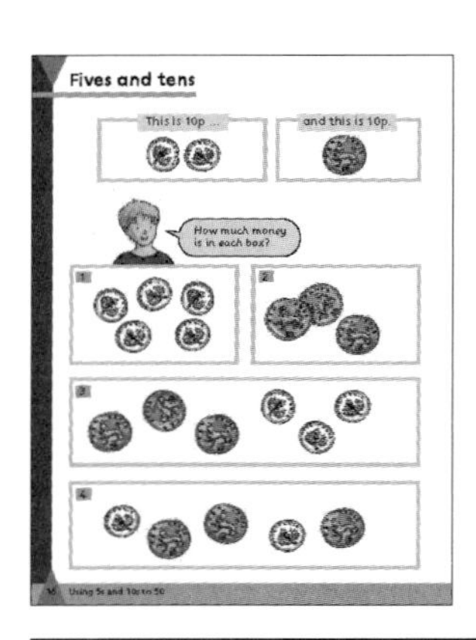

Fives and tens

This is 10p ... and this is 10p.

How much money is in each box?

1

2

3

4

16 Using 5s and 10s to 50

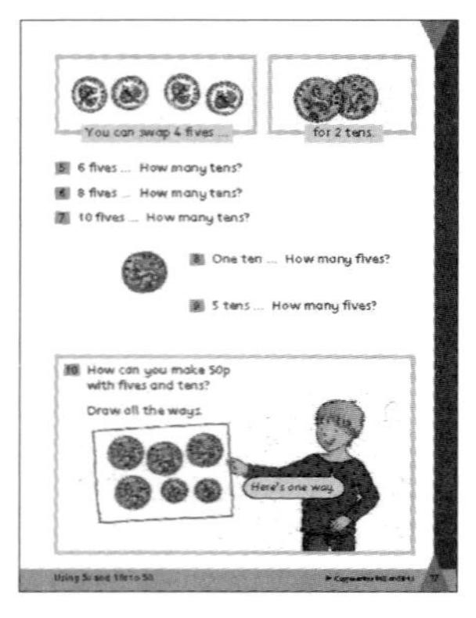

You can swap 4 fives ... for 2 tens.

5 6 fives ... How many tens?

6 8 fives ... How many tens?

7 10 fives ... How many tens?

8 One ten ... How many fives?

9 5 tens ... How many fives?

10 How can you make 50p with fives and tens?

Draw all the ways.

Here's one way.

Using 5s and 10s to 50

Textbook pages 16 and 17

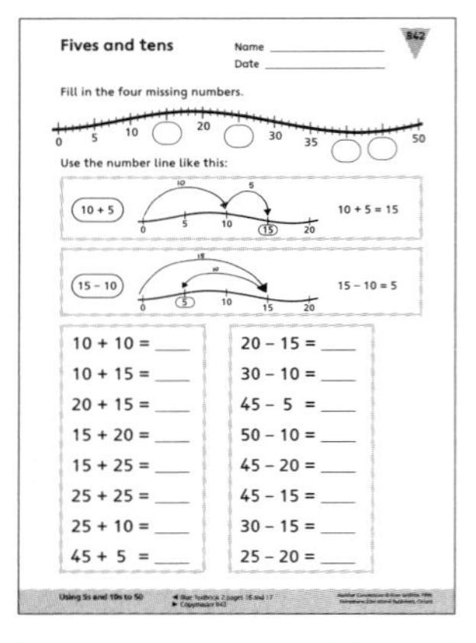

Fives and tens Name ______ Date ______ B42

Fill in the four missing numbers.

0 5 10 ◯ 20 ◯ 30 35 ◯ ◯ 50

Use the number line like this:

10 + 5 → 10 + 5 = 15

15 − 10 → 15 − 10 = 5

10 + 10 = ____	20 − 15 = ____
10 + 15 = ____	30 − 10 = ____
20 + 15 = ____	45 − 5 = ____
15 + 20 = ____	50 − 10 = ____
15 + 25 = ____	45 − 20 = ____
25 + 25 = ____	45 − 15 = ____
25 + 10 = ____	30 − 15 = ____
45 + 5 = ____	25 − 20 = ____

Using 5s and 10s to 50

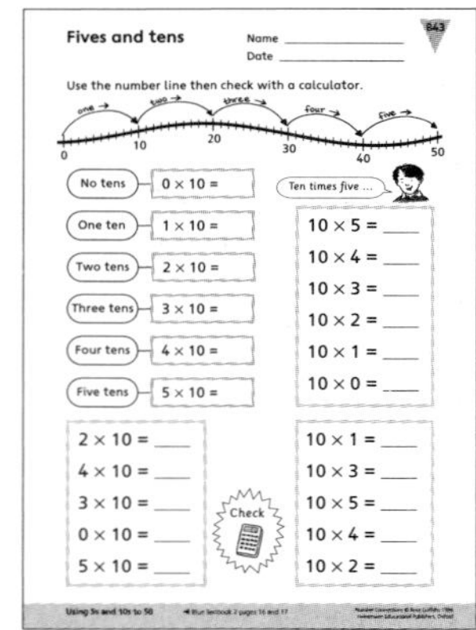

Fives and tens Name ______ Date ______ B43

Use the number line then check with a calculator.

one → two → three → four → five →

0 10 20 30 40 50

No tens — 0 × 10 =

One ten — 1 × 10 =

Two tens — 2 × 10 =

Three tens — 3 × 10 =

Four tens — 4 × 10 =

Five tens — 5 × 10 =

Ten times five ...

10 × 5 = ____
10 × 4 = ____
10 × 3 = ____
10 × 2 = ____
10 × 1 = ____
10 × 0 = ____

2 × 10 = ____	10 × 1 = ____
4 × 10 = ____	10 × 3 = ____
3 × 10 = ____	10 × 5 = ____
0 × 10 = ____	10 × 4 = ____
5 × 10 = ____	10 × 2 = ____

Check

Using 5s and 10s to 50

Copymasters B42 and B43

Purpose

Practising exchanging two 5p coins for a 10p coin

Looking at the links between 5s and 10s

Improving fluency in counting in 5s and in 10s, to 50

Materials

Calculator

50p in 10p coins and 50p in 5p coins

Supporting activity

- Work with a partner. One person should start with 50p in 10p coins, and the other with 50p in 5ps. Take turns in giving money to your partner. They have to give you the same amount back, but using different coins.

Using the textbook pages

Children practised counting in fives to 50 and, separately, in tens to 50 in Blue Textbook 1. These pages concentrate on the links between fives and tens.

Provide coins for children to use if they want to, especially for questions 6 to 10.

If you feel a child still needs considerable practice at counting in fives, let them play the 'Fifty pence' game, used from pages 24 and 25 onwards in Blue Textbook 1. It is also worth suggesting that they can practise at home. They need to be as fluent as possible at counting in multiples of 5 before they go on to consolidate the 'Five times table' on textbook pages 24 and 25.

Answers **1** 25p **2** 40p **3** 45p **4** 40p **5** 3 tens **6** 4 tens **7** 5 tens **8** 2 fives **9** 10 fives **10** Child's own drawings of ways of making 50p: there are 6 ways – 5 10p; 4 10p & 2 5p; 3 10p & 4 5p; 2 10p & 6 5p; 1 10p & 8 5p; 10 5p.

Using the copymasters

Copymaster B42 Make sure children understand the examples on this sheet before completing the sums, so that they can use the number line to help them if they wish.

Copymaster B43 Talk about the number line at the top of this sheet, and encourage children to use the number line and the calculator to do each question.

Textbook 2 pages 18 and 19

Speedy sums

Speedy sums

1 2 + 2 =
2 4 + 1 =
3 5 + 2 =
4 3 + 3 =
5 6 + 1 =
6 4 + 4 =
7 1 + 3 =
8 1 + 6 =
9 3 + 2 =
10 0 + 1 =
11 1 + 1 =
12 0 + 2 =
13 2 + 4 =
14 2 + 1 =
15 4 + 0 =
16 2 + 3 =
17 1 + 2 =
18 5 + 1 =
19 3 + 0 =
20 3 + 4 =

✓ or ✗

Mental recall of bonds within 9

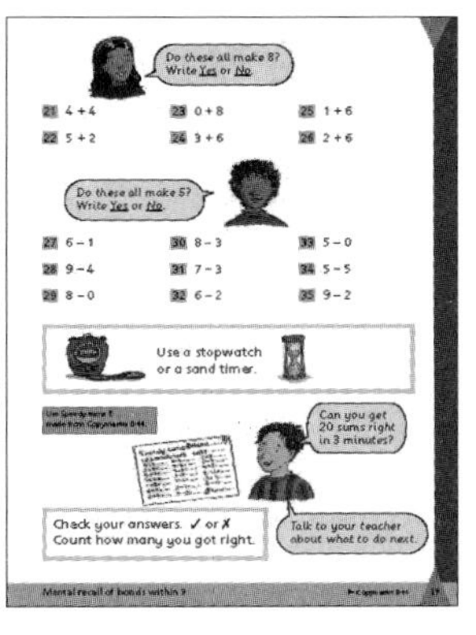

21 4 + 4
22 5 + 2
23 0 + 8
24 3 + 6
25 1 + 6
26 2 + 6

27 6 − 1
28 9 − 4
29 8 − 0
30 8 − 3
31 7 − 3
32 6 − 2
33 5 − 0
34 5 − 5
35 9 − 2

Use a stopwatch or a sand timer.

Check your answers. ✓ or ✗
Count how many you got right.

Mental recall of bonds within 9

Textbook pages 18 and 19

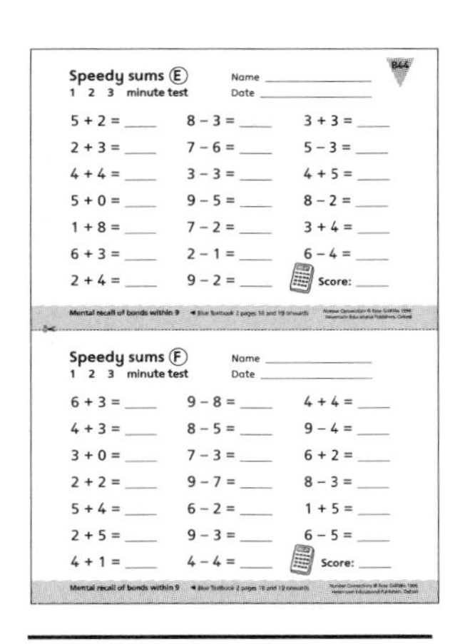

B44

Speedy sums (E)
1 2 3 minute test

Name ______
Date ______

5 + 2 = ___ 8 − 3 = ___ 3 + 3 = ___
2 + 3 = ___ 7 − 6 = ___ 5 − 3 = ___
4 + 4 = ___ 3 − 3 = ___ 4 + 5 = ___
5 + 0 = ___ 9 − 5 = ___ 8 − 2 = ___
1 + 8 = ___ 7 − 2 = ___ 3 + 4 = ___
6 + 3 = ___ 2 − 1 = ___ 6 − 4 = ___
2 + 4 = ___ 9 − 2 = ___ Score: ___

Mental recall of bonds within 9

Speedy sums (F)
1 2 3 minute test

Name ______
Date ______

6 + 3 = ___ 9 − 8 = ___ 4 + 4 = ___
4 + 3 = ___ 8 − 5 = ___ 9 − 4 = ___
3 + 0 = ___ 7 − 3 = ___ 6 + 2 = ___
2 + 2 = ___ 9 − 7 = ___ 8 − 3 = ___
5 + 4 = ___ 6 − 2 = ___ 1 + 5 = ___
2 + 5 = ___ 9 − 3 = ___ 6 − 5 = ___
4 + 1 = ___ 4 − 4 = ___ Score: ___

Mental recall of bonds within 9

Copymaster B44

Purpose

Establishing or revising addition and subtraction bonds within 9, and improving immediate mental recall of those number facts

Materials

Stopwatch or 3, 2 and 1 minute sand timers (some children may have digital watches with timers on them)
Calculator

Supporting activity

▸ Play the 'Make 9' game, made from Copymasters B60 and B61.

Using the textbook pages

These pages continue to use a series of timed tests which can be used over and over again to improve mental recall of addition and subtraction facts. The tests were first introduced in Blue Textbook 1 page 18 (for bonds within 8) and there are further tests in Textbook 3 page 14 (for bonds within 10).

Questions 1 to 20 practise addition bonds within 8. Check that children realise that knowing a sum 'off by heart' means you do not have to work it out because you remember the answer straight away. Suggest they look at each other's sums, to compare which sums they each know off by heart. Children should mark their own sums with a calculator. This will help them remember any they got wrong; it will also remind them that it is quicker to do these smaller sums in your head.

Answers **1** to **20** marked by children **21** Yes **22** No **23** Yes **24** No **25** No **26** Yes **27** Yes **28** Yes **29** No **30** Yes **31** No **32** No **33** Yes **34** No **35** No

Using the copymaster

Copymaster B44 This provides two parallel tests covering all the significant bonds within 9. Children should fill in their name and the date first, and *then* time the test. Most children will already know how to use a stopwatch or sand timer. Timing can be done by the teacher or two children can take turns at timing each other.

At first, allow children 3 minutes to do as much as they can (and ring the 3 in the top left-hand corner of the test sheet). Repeating the tests, a few days apart, is a good way of helping children learn these off by heart, and their scores usually improve quite quickly. When a child has scored 20 on a test, reduce the time when they next try it to 2 minutes, then finally, if wished, to 1 minute. Children should always be working to beat *their own* previous score, or time – *not* to beat another child. The latter can encourage cheating, and so is not as effective.

Textbook 2 pages 20 and 21

Boxes

Boxes

Shaun and Emma are playing 'Boxes'.

We take turns to draw a line.

If my line makes a box, I put my letter in it ... and draw another line.

1st game

Emma got 11 boxes.
Shaun got 9.

1 Who won, Emma or Shaun?

2 How many boxes altogether?

1 1 + 9 =

2nd game

3 How many boxes for Emma?

4 How many for Shaun?

5 How many boxes altogether?

6 Who won?

3rd game

I got 10 boxes.

No, that's not right. I got 11 boxes. 11 + 10 does not make 20.

7 How many boxes for Emma?

8 How many for Shaun?

9 How many boxes altogether?

10 Who won?

4th game

I got 12 boxes.

11 How many boxes for Shaun?

12 Who won?

Textbook pages 20 and 21

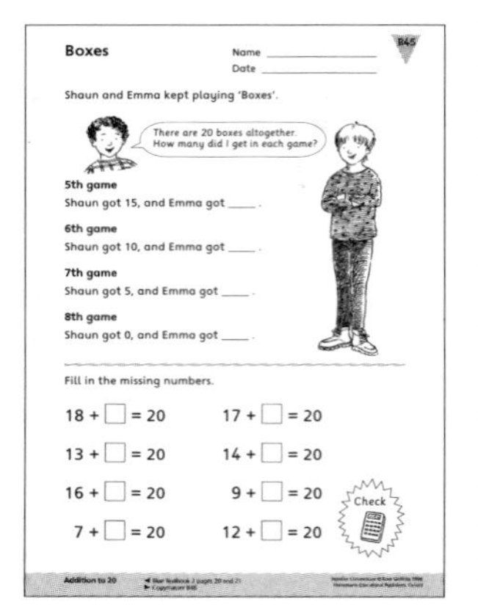

Boxes Name ______ Date ______ B45

Shaun and Emma kept playing 'Boxes'.

There are 20 boxes altogether. How many did I get in each game?

5th game
Shaun got 15, and Emma got ____.

6th game
Shaun got 10, and Emma got ____.

7th game
Shaun got 5, and Emma got ____.

8th game
Shaun got 0, and Emma got ____.

Fill in the missing numbers.

18 + ☐ = 20 17 + ☐ = 20

13 + ☐ = 20 14 + ☐ = 20

16 + ☐ = 20 9 + ☐ = 20

7 + ☐ = 20 12 + ☐ = 20

Check

Addition to 20

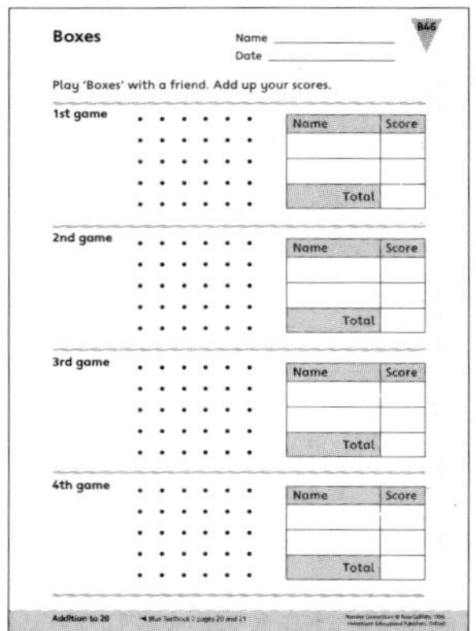

Boxes Name ______ Date ______ B46

Play 'Boxes' with a friend. Add up your scores.

1st game	Name	Score
	Total	

2nd game	Name	Score
	Total	

3rd game	Name	Score
	Total	

4th game	Name	Score
	Total	

Addition to 20

Copymasters B45 and B46

Purpose

Counting and adding to 20
Showing how to check counting by addition
Using ordinal numbers, 1st to 8th

Materials

Calculator
Square spotty paper (optional: for supporting activity)

Supporting activity

- Play small games of 'Boxes'. Use square spotty paper, or draw grids of dots measuring 3 by 3, 3 by 4, and 4 by 4. How many boxes are there altogether, for each grid? When you have finished playing, count each person's score, and add up the two scores. What do you notice?

Using the textbook pages

Make sure children understand how to play Boxes, by playing a trial game (on your own grid of dots or, if you wish, on the first grid on Copymaster B46). The first 4 games which Shaun and Emma played are shown in the textbook; the next 4 games are on Copymaster B45. Make sure children know the numerical way of writing the ordinal numbers first, second, third and so on.

Some children will realise when they are working through questions 1 to 6 that the two scores must always add up to 20 because there are 20 boxes in the grid altogether. Many children, though, will benefit from a discussion about the third game on textbook page 21. It is important that children understand this before doing Copymaster B45.

Answers **1** Emma **2** 20 **3** 5 **4** 15 **5** 20 **6** Shaun **7** 10 **8** 10 **9** 20 **10** It was a draw **11** 8 **12** Emma

Using the copymasters

Copymaster B45 If children do not seem confident that the scores for each game must add up to 20, it is sensible to give them a copy of Copymaster B46 to do *before* they tackle this sheet.

Many children will answer these questions by 'adding on'; some will use 'trial and improvement', i.e. they will make a guess, see whether that works, and then adjust it accordingly. It is unlikely that children will use subtraction, and it is better to let them choose their own method of calculation at this stage.

Copymaster B46 This sheet can be repeated as often as you wish.

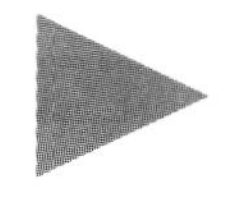

Textbook 2 pages 22 and 23

Teen numbers

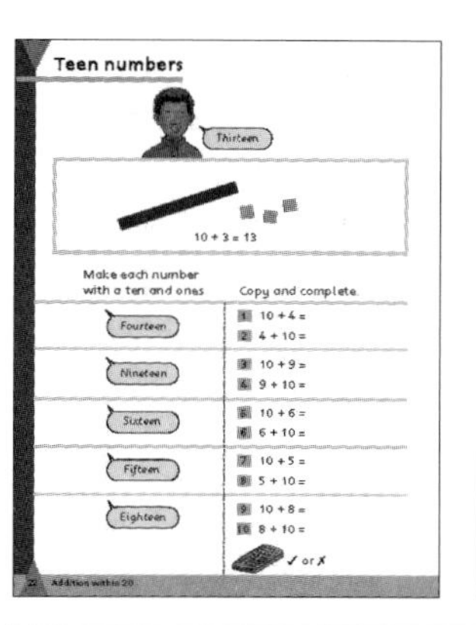

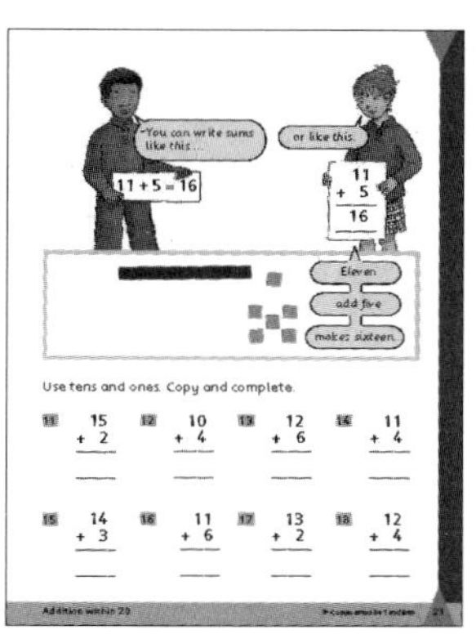

Textbook pages 22 and 23

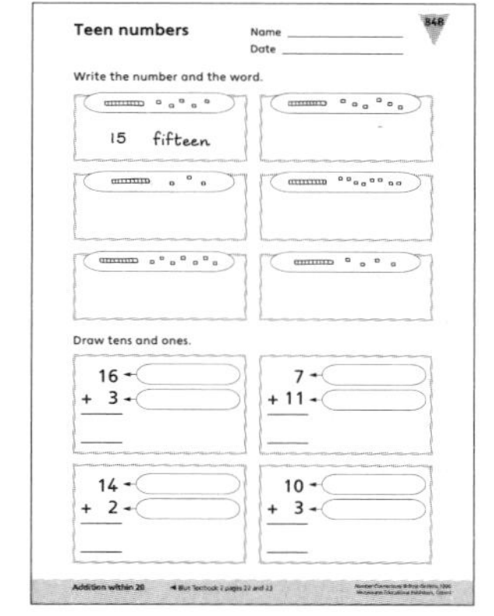

Copymasters B47 and B48

Purpose

Making numbers to 20 with base 10 equipment
Practising drawing numbers made from tens and ones
Using tens and ones to add numbers within 20
Introducing a vertical layout for addition

Materials

Structured equipment in tens and ones (such as Multibase or Dienes')

Supporting activity

► Work with a friend. Make a number from 1 to 20 using tens and ones. Your friend has to write down the number and the word (like the activity on Copymaster B48). Then your friend makes a number, and you write it.

Using the textbook pages

The use of structured equipment was introduced in 'Tens and ones' on textbook pages 8 and 9. These pages help children see that numbers from ten to twenty can be thought of as a ten and some ones. Textbook page 22 also reminds children that you should get the same answer whichever order you add up in.

Questions 1 to 10 help develop children's understanding of place value because they begin to see that, for example, the 1 in 14 stands for 10.

Textbook page 23 introduces the standard method of writing a sum down in a vertical format. Children should be expected to use equipment to work out these sums, but some children may be happy to work out some of them using their fingers or in their heads.

This work will be followed up in 'More teen numbers' on textbook pages 26 and 27.

Answers **1** 14 **2** 14 **3** 19 **4** 19 **5** 16 **6** 16 **7** 15 **8** 15 **9** 18 **10** 18 **11** 17 **12** 14 **13** 18 **14** 15 **15** 17 **16** 17 **17** 15 **18** 16

Using the copymasters

Copymaster B47 Drawing the tens and ones equipment is useful not just as a way of showing what children have done with the equipment, but also, later on, as an alternative to using it.

Copymaster B48 The first part of this sheet combines practice using the tens and ones equipment, with revising the spellings learnt in 'Sums in words' on textbook pages 6 and 7. The last four questions can be done using tens and ones equipment, or just by drawing.

Textbook 2 pages 24 and 25

Five times table

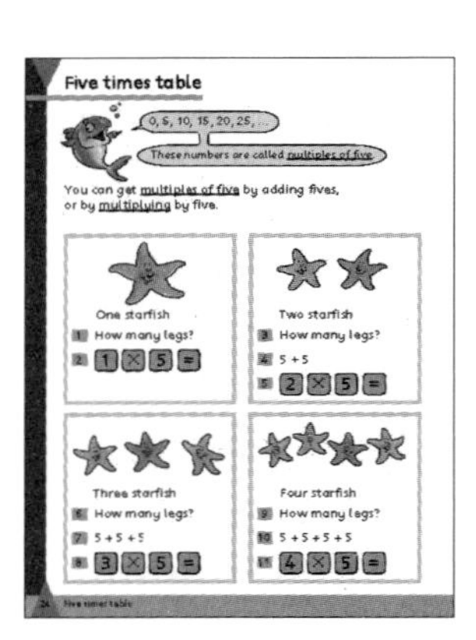

Five times table

0, 5, 10, 15, 20, 25, ...

These numbers are called multiples of five.

You can get multiples of five by adding fives, or by multiplying by five.

One starfish
How many legs?

Two starfish
How many legs?
5 + 5

Three starfish
How many legs?
5 + 5 + 5

Four starfish
How many legs?
5 + 5 + 5 + 5

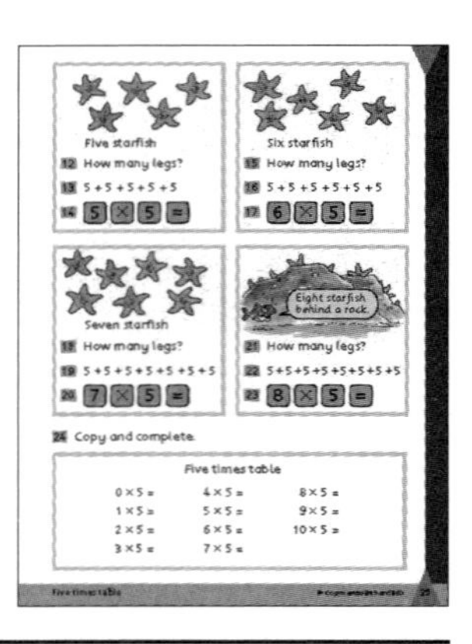

Five starfish
How many legs?
5 + 5 + 5 + 5 + 5

Six starfish
How many legs?
5 + 5 + 5 + 5 + 5 + 5

Seven starfish
How many legs?
5 + 5 + 5 + 5 + 5 + 5 + 5

Eight starfish behind a rock.
How many legs?
5 + 5 + 5 + 5 + 5 + 5 + 5 + 5

Copy and complete.

Five times table

0 × 5 = 4 × 5 = 8 × 5 =
1 × 5 = 5 × 5 = 9 × 5 =
2 × 5 = 6 × 5 = 10 × 5 =
3 × 5 = 7 × 5 =

Textbook pages 24 and 25

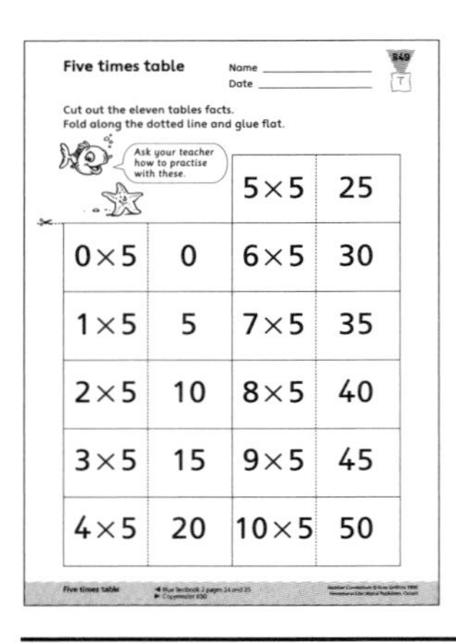

Five times table Name ______ Date ______

Cut out the eleven tables facts.
Fold along the dotted line and glue flat.

Ask your teacher how to practise with these.

		5×5	25
0×5	0	6×5	30
1×5	5	7×5	35
2×5	10	8×5	40
3×5	15	9×5	45
4×5	20	10×5	50

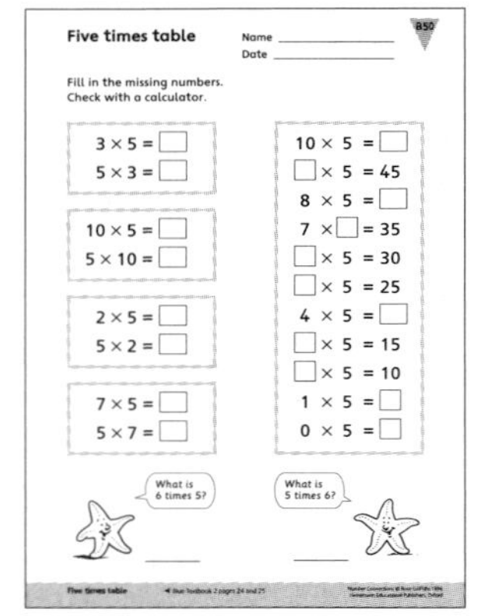

Five times table Name ______ Date ______

Fill in the missing numbers.
Check with a calculator.

3 × 5 = □
5 × 3 = □
10 × 5 = □
5 × 10 = □
2 × 5 = □
5 × 2 = □
7 × 5 = □
5 × 7 = □

10 × 5 = □
□ × 5 = 45
8 × 5 = □
7 × □ = 35
□ × 5 = 30
□ × 5 = 25
4 × 5 = □
□ × 5 = 15
□ × 5 = 10
1 × 5 = □
0 × 5 = □

What is 6 times 5?
What is 5 times 6?

Copymasters B49 and B50

Purpose

Establishing and beginning to learn the 5 times table facts
Practising the words 'multiples' and 'multiplying'

Materials

Calculator
Scissors and glue (glue stick)
Envelope (to keep tables cards in)

Supporting activities

- Practise counting from 0 to 50 in fives out loud, then back from 50 to 0.
- Use the cards made from Copymaster B49 to practise the five times table.

Using the textbook pages

Questions 1 to 20 emphasise each table fact through a picture (on which children can count the legs), by adding 5 over and over again, and by using a calculator to multiply. Children can see that, whichever way you work it out, the answer is the same. Make sure that children realise that, for example, adding 6 lots of 5 together gives you the same answer as working out 6 × 5.

Question 21 removes the pictorial support, and children have to imagine the legs to count them, or use a previous picture and add five.

It is important to include learning 0 × 5 = 0. Make sure children agree that if there are no starfish, there are no legs.

Answers **1** 5 **2** 5 **3** 10 **4** 10 **5** 10 **6** 15 **7** 15 **8** 15 **9** 20 **10** 20 **11** 20 **12** 25 **13** 25 **14** 25 **15** 30 **16** 30 **17** 30 **18** 35 **19** 35 **20** 35 **21** 40 **22** 40 **23** 40 **24** Child's own copy of the 5 times table

Using the copymasters

Copymaster B49 This sheet makes eleven small cards, with a tables question on one side and the answer on the other. Provide each child with an envelope to keep them in. Show children how to practise: shuffle the cards and put them in a pile, *questions* facing upwards. Answer the top question, then turn it over to see if you got it right. If you did, put it to one side; if not, put it at the bottom of the pile to try again. Then use the cards the other way up – look at the answer, and say what the question is. Use the cards as frequently as you wish. Children can work individually, or with a partner, or take them home to practise.

Copymaster B50 Children who feel confident can use this sheet as a test. Those who still need support should use a calculator to check each fact as they go along.

Textbook 2 pages 26 and 27

More teen numbers

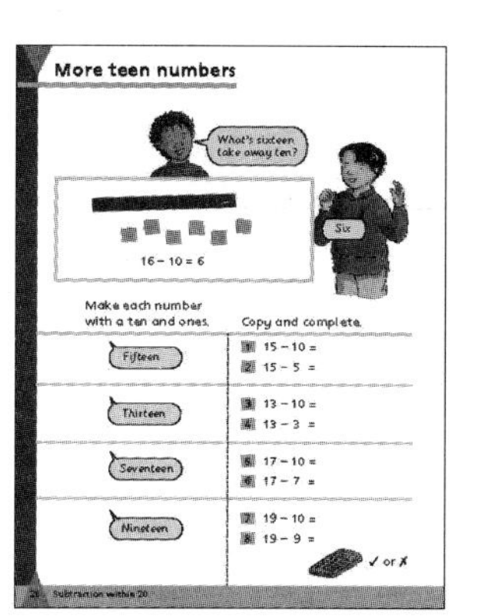

Textbook pages 26 and 27

Copymaster B51

Purpose

Making numbers to 20 with base 10 equipment, and drawing them
Using tens and ones to subtract numbers within 20
Introducing a vertical layout for subtraction

Materials

Structured equipment in tens and ones (such as Multibase or Dienes')
Calculator

Supporting activity

► Work with a friend. Make a number from 10 to 20 using tens and ones. Say the number out loud. Then shut your eyes while your friend hides some of the tens or ones from your number. Open your eyes; work out what is missing. Take turns at this.

Using the textbook pages

These pages follow the work done with addition in 'Teen numbers' on textbook pages 22 and 23.

Questions 1 to 10 help develop children's understanding of place value by taking away amounts just from the units place or just from the tens place in a number. They also emphasise the links between two numbers and their total: for example, between ten, five and fifteen. Because 10 + 5 = 15, when you take away 5 or 10 from 15, you will always get the other one as the answer.

Textbook page 27 shows the standard method of writing a subtraction in a vertical format. On a textbook page it is more difficult to show what happens when you take away than it is to explain adding. Two methods are used in this section; *arrows* on the photograph on textbook page 27, to show which pieces of equipment are taken away, and *crossing out* on the drawings of tens and ones on Copymaster B51.

Children should be expected to use equipment to work out these sums, but some children may be happy to work out some of them using their fingers or in their heads.

Answers **1** 5 **2** 10 **3** 3 **4** 10 **5** 7 **6** 10 **7** 9 **8** 10 **9** 15 **10** 4 **11** 11 **12** 10 **13** 12 **14** 11 **15** 15 **16** 7

Using the copymaster

Copymaster B51 Use tens and ones to make sure children understand how the first question can be done, and to show how the drawing (and crossing out) is used.

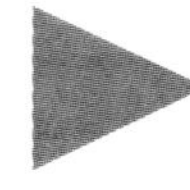

Textbook 2 pages 28 and 29

Photos

Photos

I can take 24 photos with this film.

1 I've taken 2 photos. How many more can I take?

2 Now I've taken 4 photos. How many more can I take?

3 Now I've taken 12 photos. How many more can I take?

4 Now I've taken 17 photos. How many more can I take?

5 Now I've taken 20 photos. How many more can I take?

6 Now I've taken 24 photos. How many more can I take?

Addition and subtraction within 24

You took 14 photos of your cat, 2 photos of your finger, and 8 photos of me!

7 Check the total. 14 + 2 + 8

8 These all make 24.

14 + 2 + 8 = 24
12 + 12 = 24
20 + 4 = 24
10 + 10 + 4 = 24

Write ten more sums which make 24.

Ask a friend to check. ✓ or ✗

Addition and subtraction within 24

Textbook pages 28 and 29

Photos Name ______ Date ______ B52

I took 24 photos.

How many photos of the rabbit? ______

How many photos of my friends? ______

Total: ______

I took 24 photos.

How many photos of the dog? ______

How many photos of my friends? ______

Total: ______

Check

Addition and subtraction within 24

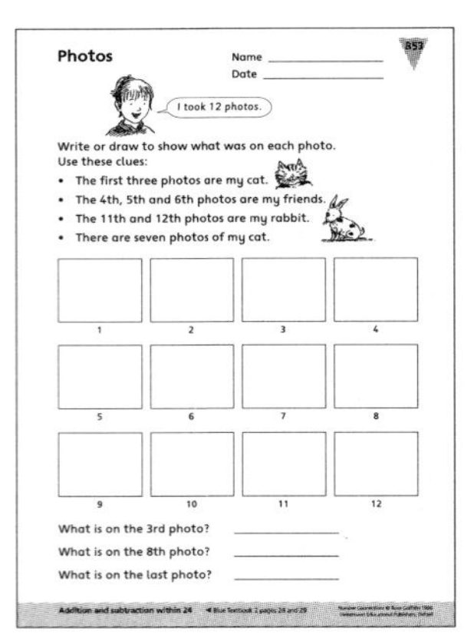

Photos Name ______ Date ______ B53

I took 12 photos.

Write or draw to show what was on each photo.
Use these clues:

- The first three photos are my cat.
- The 4th, 5th and 6th photos are my friends.
- The 11th and 12th photos are my rabbit.
- There are seven photos of my cat.

1 2 3 4
5 6 7 8
9 10 11 12

What is on the 3rd photo? ______

What is on the 8th photo? ______

What is on the last photo? ______

Addition and subtraction within 24

Copymasters B52 and B53

Purpose

Counting and adding to 24; subtraction within 24
Showing how to check counting by addition
Using ordinal numbers, 1st to 12th

Materials

Calculator
Photos and matching negatives (optional: for supporting activity)

Supporting activity

- ► Look at some photos and their negatives. Look for the numbers on the negatives, which tell you the order the photos were taken in. If possible, look at a camera and see how you can tell how many photos have been taken.

(NB Notice that when the indicator on a camera says, for example, '20', it means you have taken 19 photos and the next one is the 20th.)

Using the textbook pages

Most children have used a camera, and will enjoy talking about some of the photos they have taken before starting these pages, which follow the ideas raised in 'Boxes' on textbook pages 20 and 21.

Children can use the film drawn at the top of textbook page 28 as though it were a number line. Most children will work out the answers to questions 1 to 6 by 'counting on' rather than by taking away.

The first part of textbook page 29, which looks at checking your counting by adding up to see if it makes 24, leads on to the work on Copymaster B52. The second part of the textbook page introduces children to looking at ways of making 24 by adding.

Answers **1** 22 **2** 20 **3** 12 **4** 7 **5** 4 **6** 0 **7** 24 **8** Child's own examples

Using the copymasters

Copymaster B52 Counting and checking that the total comes to 24, following on from the work done about games of Boxes on Copymaster B46.

Copymaster B53 This sheet requires children to think about the clues they are given and to work logically. Children should work in pencil, in case of mistakes, and they may enjoy working with a friend to discuss what to do.

Textbook 2 pages 30 and 31

Hopping frogs

Hopping frogs

We score 3 points for each frog in the dish.

3 + 3 + 3 = 9
9 points

What did we score?

1 2 frogs in the dish. 3 + 3 = ___

2 4 frogs in the dish.

3 5 frogs in the dish.

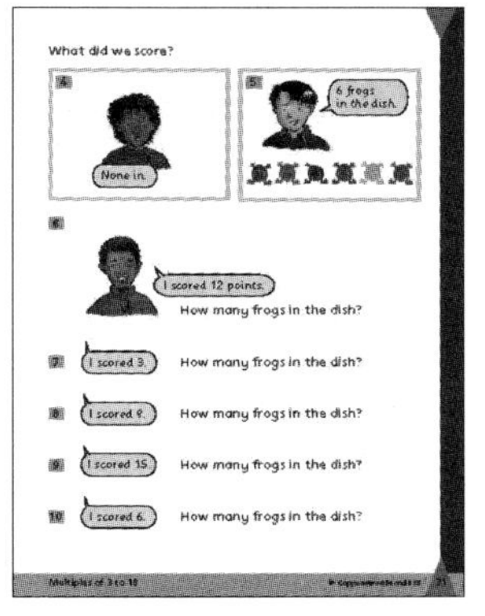

What did we score?

4 None in.

5 6 frogs in the dish.

6 I scored 12 points. How many frogs in the dish?

7 I scored 3. How many frogs in the dish?

8 I scored 9. How many frogs in the dish?

9 I scored 15. How many frogs in the dish?

10 I scored 6. How many frogs in the dish?

Textbook pages 30 and 31

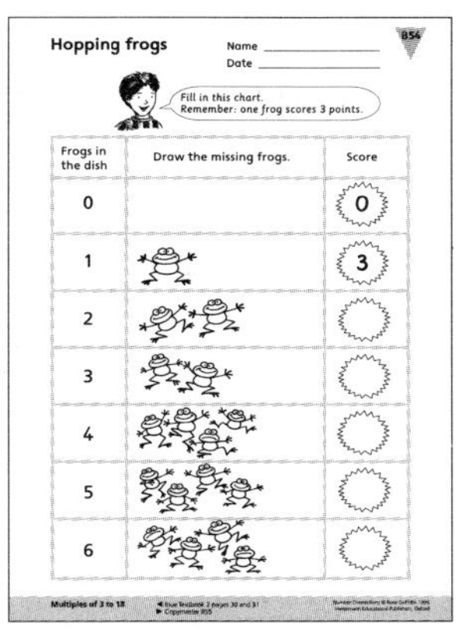

Hopping frogs Name ___ Date ___ B54

Fill in this chart.
Remember: one frog scores 3 points.

Frogs in the dish	Draw the missing frogs.	Score
0		0
1		3
2		
3		
4		
5		
6		

Multiples of 3 to 18

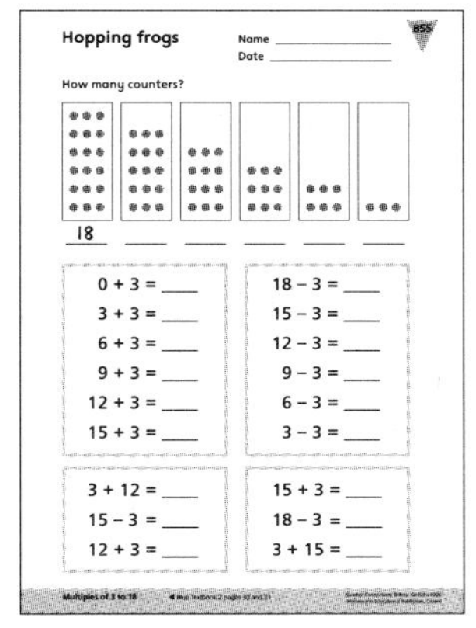

Hopping frogs Name ___ Date ___ B55

How many counters?

18 ___ ___ ___ ___ ___

0 + 3 = ___	18 − 3 = ___
3 + 3 = ___	15 − 3 = ___
6 + 3 = ___	12 − 3 = ___
9 + 3 = ___	9 − 3 = ___
12 + 3 = ___	6 − 3 = ___
15 + 3 = ___	3 − 3 = ___
3 + 12 = ___	15 + 3 = ___
15 − 3 = ___	18 − 3 = ___
12 + 3 = ___	3 + 15 = ___

Multiples of 3 to 18

Copymasters B54 and B55

Purpose

Establishing and practising multiples of 3 to 18
Using a chart

Materials

'Hopping frogs' game (optional: for supporting activity)

Supporting activity

- Play 'Hopping frogs' with a game bought from a toy shop, or using counters as tiddlywinks. Score 3 points for each frog you get in a saucer or dish.

Using the textbook pages

Counting in threes to 12 was practised in Red Textbook 2, in 'Threes' on pages 30 and 31. The best introduction to these pages is to play 'Hopping frogs'.

Questions 1 to 5 are worked out by repeated addition (which leads to multiplication). Questions 6 to 10 look at the multiples of 3 'the other way round', ie they are leading towards division by 3. Most children will probably answer questions 6 to 10 by using trial and improvement; they will have a guess, see if it works, and if it does not, try a bigger or smaller number. Alternatively, some children will realise that they can look back at their answers to questions 1 to 5 to help them.

Answers **1** 6 **2** 12 **3** 15 **4** 0 **5** 18 **6** 4 **7** 1 **8** 3 **9** 5 **10** 2

Using the copymasters

Copymaster B54 Filling in a chart to present information in an organised way is an important skill, and helps children recognise and learn number patterns and facts. Make sure children realise that the first box under the heading 'Draw the missing frogs' is meant to stay empty, because it is the line in the chart for no frogs.

Copymaster B55 To help with the sums at the bottom of the sheet, children can use the dots arranged in rows of three at the beginning of the sheet. Adding and taking away in threes helps children memorise the numbers 0, 3, 6, 9, 12, 15 and 18.

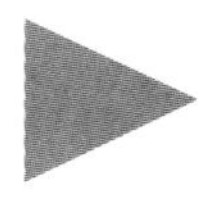

Textbook 2 page 32

Make £15

Make £15

Work with a friend if you want to.
Make a £10 note and three £5 notes.
Collect fifteen '£1 coins'. or

Combinations of 1, 5 and 10 to make 15

Textbook page 32

Purpose

Practising addition to 15
Beginning to work more systematically

Materials

A '£10 note', three '£5 notes' and fifteen '£1 coins' (e.g. counters or token coins)

Using the textbook page

Children may approach the problem posed by this page in several ways. Most children will seem to work very randomly; they will think of one way of making £15, make it with the coins and notes, and draw it, and then try to find more ways, but without any particular system of working, so they may never be sure they have found all the possible ways. It is better not to try to impose a particular method on the children, but instead encourage them to check systematically that they have not repeated a way, and that each way does come to £15.

Many children like working with a partner for this activity, as they can check each other's addition and exchange ideas about finding more ways of making £15. They can also discuss whether, for example, a £5 note and a £10 note counts as the same as a £10 note and a £5 note. (Most people would feel it is the same.)

Incidentally, this activity provides an opportunity to see whether children are writing £ signs clearly. If not, you could ask them to repeat Copymasters R76 and R77, from Red Textbook 3 pages 18 and 19.

Answers There are 6 ways of making £15 from these notes and coins:
15 £1 coins; 10 £1 coins and 1 £5 note: 5 £1 coins and 2 £5 notes; 5 £1 coins and 1 £10 note; 1 £5 note and 1 £10 note; 3 £5 notes

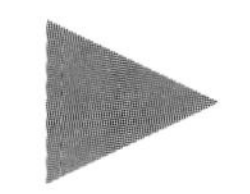

Blue Textbook 3 / Copymasters B62–B92

Contents

■ (grey) Counting and place value

■ (black) Addition and subtraction

● (black) Multiplication and division

● (grey) Mixed operations

Textbook 3 pages 4 and 5

Joke shop

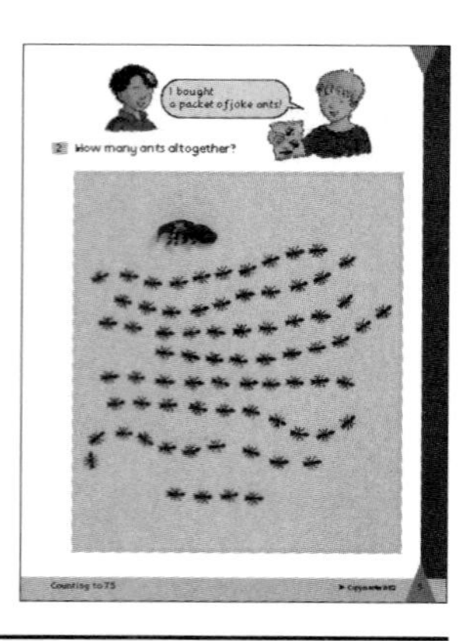

Textbook pages 4 and 5

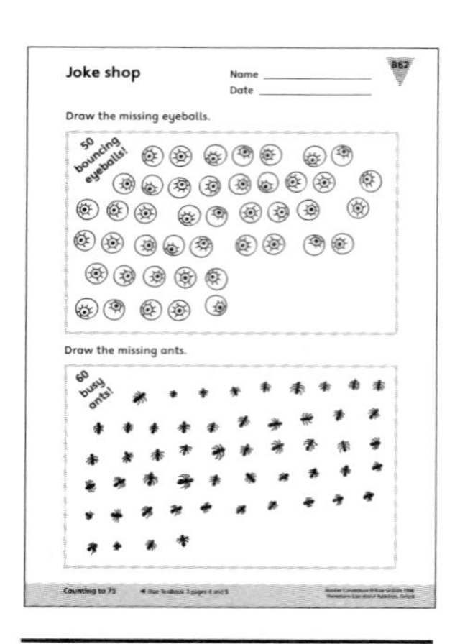

Copymaster B62

Purpose

Practising counting numbers of objects, up to 75

Materials

75 counters or other small objects (optional: for supporting activity)

Supporting activity

► Use some counters or other small objects. Count out 75 of them, one at a time; then count them again, putting them in piles of ten to help you. Which way of counting is easiest?

Using the textbook pages

Talk to children about whether they have ever had joke biscuits or other items like these, before starting work on these pages.

Most children count the biscuits on textbook page 4 a row at a time, across the page. Once they have written down their answer, suggest they count again, working down the page, a column at a time. There are 6 biscuits in each row, and 10 in each column.

The ants on textbook page 5 might seem harder to count, because they are not in straight lines. However, they are arranged in groups of ten, to help.

(NB Any child who has difficulty counting the amounts in questions 1 and 2 should be given further practical work, to increase their skill at counting numbers up to 75, *before* continuing with work in this book. Blue Textbook 2 includes activities and games which practise counting up to 60.)

Answers The joke biscuit is in the 7th row from the top and the 4th column from the left. **1** 60 **2** 74

Using the copymaster

Copymaster B62 Children may find it helps to draw round groups of ten to make it easier to count the eyeballs or spiders, before they draw the missing ones.

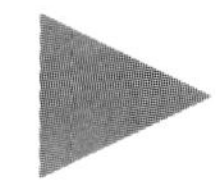

Textbook 3 pages 6 and 7

Tens and teens

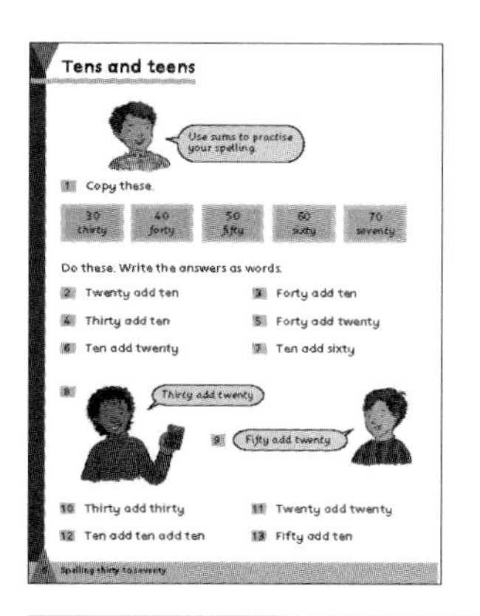

Tens and teens

Use sums to practise your spelling.

1 Copy these.

30 thirty 40 forty 50 fifty 60 sixty 70 seventy

Do these. Write the answers as words.

2 Twenty add ten
3 Forty add ten
4 Thirty add ten
5 Forty add twenty
6 Ten add twenty
7 Ten add sixty
8 Thirty add twenty
9 Fifty add twenty
10 Thirty add thirty
11 Twenty add twenty
12 Ten add ten add ten
13 Fifty add ten

Spelling thirty to seventy

4 four 4th fourth 14 fourteen 40 forty

Forty does not have a u.

Write these numbers as words.

14 4 15 14 16 40 17 4th

When you say 13 and 30 the first part sounds the same.

Work with a friend.
Say these out loud, then write the numbers as words.

18 17 and 70 19 15 and 50
20 14 and 40 21 16 and 60
22 13 and 30

Ask your teacher if you can play 'Tens and teens bingo'.

Spelling thirty to seventy

Textbook pages 6 and 7

Tens and teens Name Date B63

Fill in the missing letters.

30 thirty thir__ th__ t__ thirty
40 forty for__ f__ forty
50 fifty fif__ fi__ f__ fifty
60 sixty six__ si__ s__ sixty
70 seventy seven__ sev__ s__ seventy

Mixed up numbers! Sort them out.

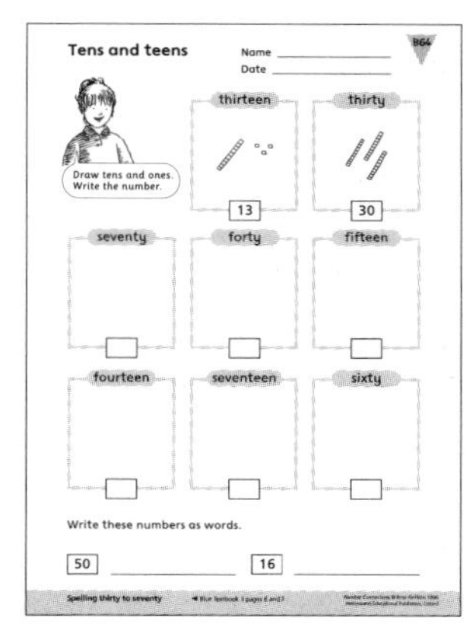

Tens and teens Name Date B64

Draw tens and ones. Write the number.

thirteen 13 thirty 30
seventy forty fifteen
fourteen seventeen sixty

Write these numbers as words.

50 16

Copymasters B63, B64, B88 and B89

Purpose

Learning and practising the spellings of thirty to seventy
Adding in tens within seventy
Distinguishing between commonly confused numbers (e.g. 13 and 30)

Materials

Calculator

Supporting activity

► Play 'Tens and teens bingo'. See Copymasters B88 and B89 below.

Using the textbook pages

In Blue Textbook 2 pages 6 and 7, children practised spelling numbers up to 20. You may wish to revise those before starting these pages. The main point of questions 1 to 13 is to practise reading and spelling the numbers as words; the questions can be done with a calculator, if wished. Questions 14 to 17 point out the important difference when spelling forty (i.e. no 'u').

Questions 18 to 22 will help many children begin to deal more confidently with these pairs of words which are often confused. It is helpful to tell children that adults often have to ask people to say these numbers again, to make sure they have heard correctly, and sometimes people will say, for example, 'Thirteen, that's one, three' to be absolutely clear. Children for whom English is an additional language may need more practice in listening to and saying the pairs.

Answers **1** Child's own copy of spellings **2** Thirty **3** Fifty **4** Forty **5** Sixty **6** Thirty **7** Seventy **8** Fifty **9** Seventy **10** Sixty **11** Forty **12** Thirty **13** Sixty **14** Four **15** Fourteen **16** Forty **17** Fourth **18** Seventeen and seventy **19** Fifteen and fifty **20** Fourteen and forty **21** Sixteen and sixty **22** Thirteen and thirty

Using the copymasters

Copymaster B63 This provides spelling practice which concentrates on a different part of each word at a time. The mixed-up numbers can be used to focus attention on how many letters there are in each word, and on any distinctive letters (for example, that there is an 'f' in 'forty'). The sheet can be repeated if needed.

Copymaster B64 Drawing the tens and ones you would use to make each number reinforces the difference between the multiples of ten and the numbers in the teens. Children can use tens and ones to make each number, then copy it.

Copymasters B88 and B89 The 'Tens and teens bingo' game, which practises saying, listening to, and reading each hard-to-distinguish number, can be played as many times as you wish from here onwards.

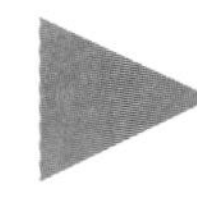

Textbook 3 pages 8 and 9

What comes next?

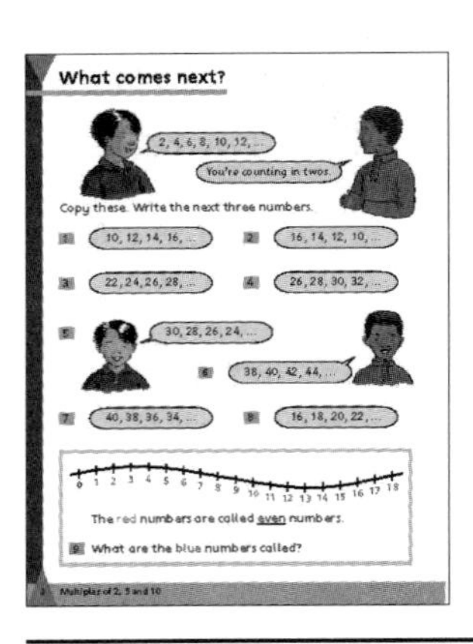

What comes next?

2, 4, 6, 8, 10, 12, ...

You're counting in twos.

Copy these. Write the next three numbers.

1 10, 12, 14, 16, ... 2 16, 14, 12, 10, ...

3 22, 24, 26, 28, ... 4 26, 28, 30, 32, ...

5 30, 28, 26, 24, ...

6 38, 40, 42, 44, ...

7 40, 38, 36, 34, ... 8 16, 18, 20, 22, ...

0 1 2 3 4 5 6 7 8 9 10 11 12 13 14 15 16 17 18

The red numbers are called even numbers.

9 What are the blue numbers called?

Multiples of 2, 5 and 10

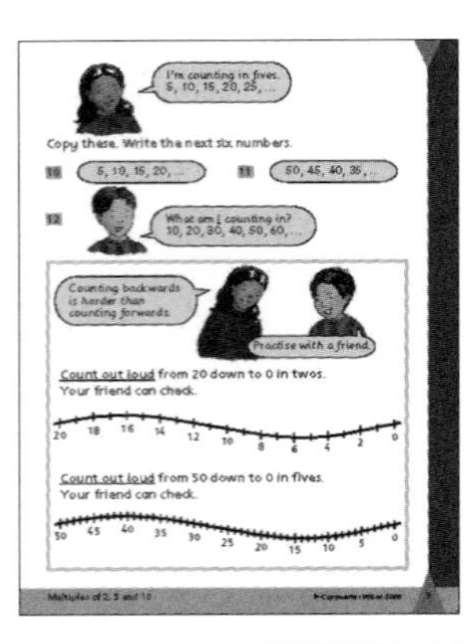

I'm counting in fives. 5, 10, 15, 20, 25, ...

Copy these. Write the next six numbers.

10 5, 10, 15, 20, ... 11 50, 45, 40, 35, ...

12 What am I counting in? 10, 20, 30, 40, 50, 60, ...

Counting backwards is harder than counting forwards.

Practise with a friend.

Count out loud from 20 down to 0 in twos. Your friend can check.

20 18 16 14 12 10 8 6 4 2 0

Count out loud from 50 down to 0 in fives. Your friend can check.

50 45 40 35 30 25 20 15 10 5 0

Multiples of 2, 5 and 10

Textbook pages 8 and 9

What comes next? Name ______ Date ______ B65

Join the dots. They go up in twos.

Join the dots. They go up in fives.

Join the dots. They go up in tens.

Draw eyes and whiskers.

Join the dots. They go down in fives.

Draw eyes and a nose.

Multiples of 2, 5 and 10

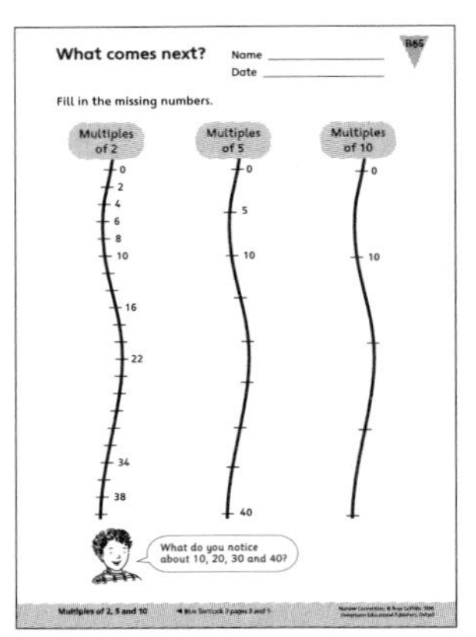

What comes next? Name ______ Date ______

Fill in the missing numbers.

Multiples of 2	Multiples of 5	Multiples of 10
0, 2, 4, 6, 8, 10, 16, 22, 34, 38	0, 5, 10, 40	0, 10

What do you notice about 10, 20, 30 and 40?

Multiples of 2, 5 and 10

Copymasters B65 and B66

Purpose

Improving fluency with multiples of 2, 5 and 10
Revising odd and even numbers
Realising that some numbers are multiples of 2, 5 and 10

Materials

Number line from 0 to 40 or more (optional: for supporting activity)

Supporting activities

- Practise counting forwards and backwards in 2s, 5s or 10s on a number line to 40 (or more).
- Ask a friend to listen to you counting out loud, but do not tell them whether you are counting in 2s, 5s or 10s. How quickly can they tell you if you are counting forwards or backwards, and whether you are counting in 2s, 5s or 10s?

Using the textbook pages

Each of these multiples has been practised before; these pages look at them together, to encourage children to focus on which is which, and to see that all the numbers which are multiples of 10 are also multiples of 2 and 5. With some children, it will be necessary to revise the fact that, for example, if we are counting in 2s we can work out which numbers come next by adding on 2, over and over again.

Practice at counting out loud both forwards and backwards is very important, and can be a useful whole-group activity. Counting backwards in 2s or 5s is quite difficult, and you may need to go slowly and provide a number line to help.

Answers **1** 18, 20, 22 **2** 8, 6, 4 **3** 30, 32, 34 **4** 34, 36, 37 **5** 22, 20, 18 **6** 46, 48, 50 **7** 32, 30, 28 **8** 24, 26, 28 **9** Odd numbers **10** 25, 30, 35, 40, 45, 50 **11** 30, 25, 20, 15, 10, 5 **12** Tens

Using the copymasters

Copymaster B65 The first three dot-to-dot puzzles here go 'forwards', and the child is expected to start at 0. On the last picture, make sure children realise they should start at 50 and count *down* in 5s.

Copymaster B66 This sheet presents three number lines, each showing just one set of multiples. They are aligned so that children can begin to see that some numbers are multiples of 2, 5 and 10. Children may also notice that when you are counting in 2s, it takes a lot of steps to get to 40, whereas counting in 10s takes less steps.

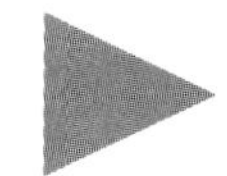

Textbook 3 pages 10 and 11

Footballs

Footballs

"£9, please."

1 How much change?

Copy and complete.

2 10 − 9 =

3 9 + □ = 10

"£8, please."

4 How much change?

5 10 − 8 =

6 8 + □ = 10

"£7, please."

7 How much change?

8 10 − 7 =

9 7 + □ = 10

Addition and subtraction bonds to 10

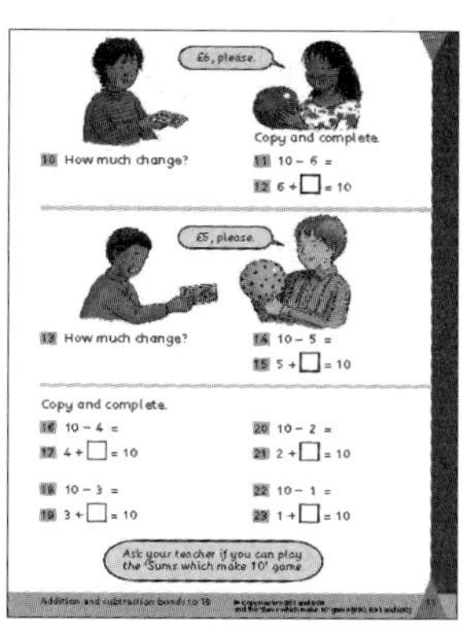

"£6, please."

10 How much change?

Copy and complete.

11 10 − 6 =

12 6 + □ = 10

"£5, please."

13 How much change?

14 10 − 5 =

15 5 + □ = 10

Copy and complete.

16 10 − 4 =

17 4 + □ = 10

18 10 − 3 =

19 3 + □ = 10

20 10 − 2 =

21 2 + □ = 10

22 10 − 1 =

23 1 + □ = 10

Ask your teacher if you can play the 'Sums which make 10' game.

Addition and subtraction bonds to 10

Textbook pages 10 and 11

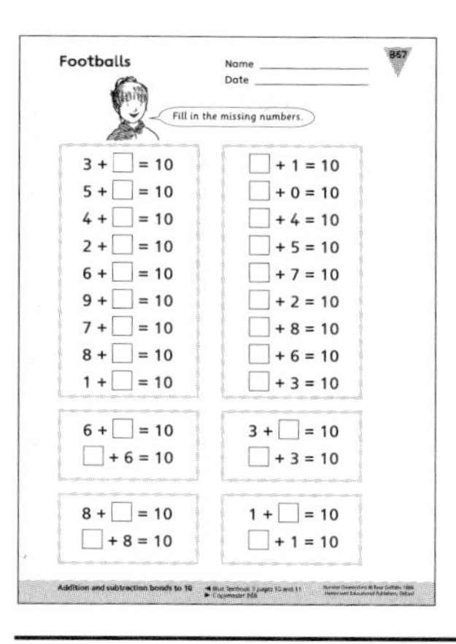

Footballs Name Date B67

Fill in the missing numbers.

3 + □ = 10	□ + 1 = 10
5 + □ = 10	□ + 0 = 10
4 + □ = 10	□ + 4 = 10
2 + □ = 10	□ + 5 = 10
6 + □ = 10	□ + 7 = 10
9 + □ = 10	□ + 2 = 10
7 + □ = 10	□ + 8 = 10
8 + □ = 10	□ + 6 = 10
1 + □ = 10	□ + 3 = 10
6 + □ = 10	3 + □ = 10
□ + 6 = 10	□ + 3 = 10
8 + □ = 10	1 + □ = 10
□ + 8 = 10	□ + 1 = 10

Addition and subtraction bonds to 10

Footballs Name Date B68

Do these as quickly as you can.

10 − 2 =	10 − 7 =	10 − 1 =
10 − 3 =	10 − 0 =	10 − 8 =
10 − 9 =	10 − 5 =	10 − 4 =
10 − 4 =	10 − 6 =	10 − 3 =
10 − 8 =	10 − 2 =	10 − 7 =

✓ or ✗

How much change?

How much change?

How much change?

How much change?

Addition and subtraction bonds to 10

Copymasters B67, B68, B90, B91 and B92

Purpose

Establishing and practising addition and subtraction bonds to 10, and improving immediate mental recall of those number facts

Materials

Ten £1 coins (or counters)
Calculator
Scissors (optional: for supporting activity)

Supporting activity

- Work with a partner. Put ten £1 coins on the table in front of you, then hide some with your hand. Your partner has to say as quickly as possible how many are hidden, Take turns at this.
- Play the 'Sums which make 10' game. See Copymasters B90, B91 and B92 below.

Using the textbook pages

Number bonds to 10 are very important, and they were practised in Red Textbook 3, in 'Make 10' on pages 12 and 13, and in Blue Textbook 1, in 'Bowling' on pages 22 and 23.

When using money, most people probably use 'counting on' rather than subtraction to work out their change. These pages remind children of the links between addition and subtraction.

Some children may need coins and a calculator to help them with these pages, but most will not. Remind children that fingers are useful when you are working with sums which make 10!

Answers **1** £1 **2** 1 **3** 1 **4** £2 **5** 2 **6** 2 **7** £3 **8** 3 **9** 3 **10** £4 **11** 4 **12** 4 **13** £5 **14** 5 **15** 5 **16** 6 **17** 6 **18** 7 **19** 7 **20** 8 **21** 8 **22** 9 **23** 9

Using the copymasters

Copymasters B67 and B68 Children who feel confident with number bonds to 10 can use these sheets as tests. Those who still need help can use their fingers. Point out the pairs of facts - for example, 6 + 4 and 4 + 6 both add up to 10; 10 − 2 = 8 and 2 + 8 = 10.

Copymasters B90, B91 and B92 The 'Sums which make 10' game is similar to the game 'Sums which make 8' on Copymasters B26, B27 and B28. It can be played as many times as you wish, from these pages onwards.

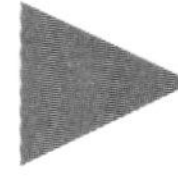

Textbook 3 pages 12 and 13

Easier adding

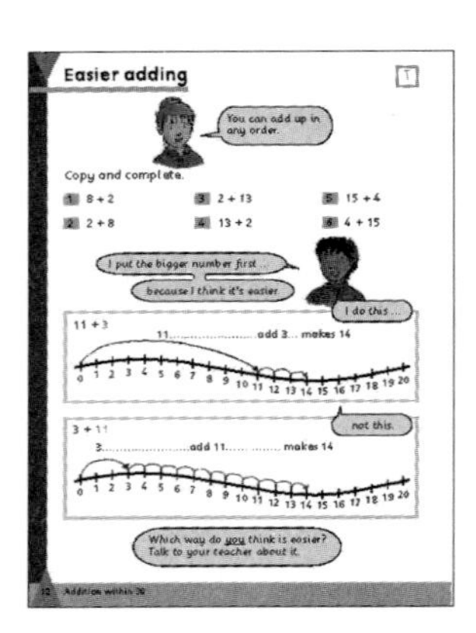

Easier adding

You can add up in any order.

Copy and complete.

1 8 + 2
2 2 + 8
3 2 + 13
4 13 + 2
5 15 + 4
6 4 + 15

I put the bigger number first ...
because I think it's easier.
I do this ...

11 + 3
11 .... add 3 ... makes 14

3 + 11
not this.
3 .... add 11 .... makes 14

Which way do you think is easier? Talk to your teacher about it.

12 Addition within 30

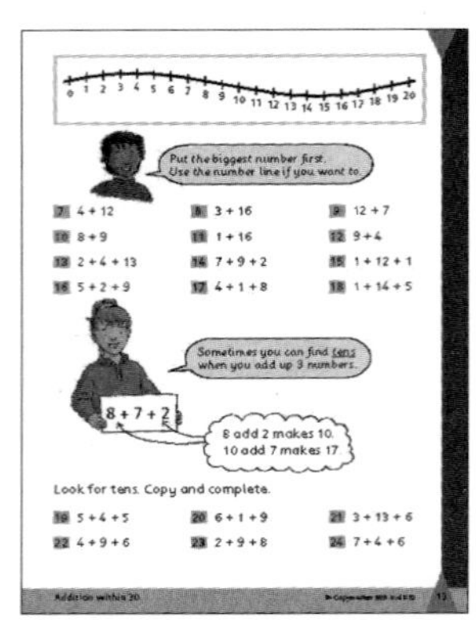

Put the biggest number first. Use the number line if you want to.

7 4 + 12
8 3 + 16
9 12 + 7
10 8 + 9
11 1 + 16
12 9 + 4
13 2 + 4 + 13
14 7 + 9 + 2
15 1 + 12 + 1
16 5 + 2 + 9
17 4 + 1 + 8
18 1 + 14 + 5

Sometimes you can find tens when you add up 3 numbers.

8 + 7 + 2

8 add 2 makes 10.
10 add 7 makes 17.

Look for tens. Copy and complete.

19 5 + 4 + 5
20 6 + 1 + 9
21 3 + 13 + 6
22 4 + 9 + 6
23 2 + 9 + 8
24 7 + 4 + 6

Addition within 30 13

Textbook pages 12 and 13

Easier adding Name ______ Date ______ B69

Find tens if you can, to help you.

4 + 9 + 1 = 14
3 + 5 + 7 = ____
2 + 8 + 9 = ____
13 + 4 + 6 = ____
5 + 9 + 5 = ____
6 + 15 + 4 = ____
8 + 11 + 2 = ____
5 + 6 + 7 = ____
9 + 1 + 13 = ____
7 + 9 + 3 = ____

7 + 2 + 3 = 12

Look for tens.

4 + 8 + 6
12 + 3 + 7
6 + 11 + 4
8 + 14 + 2

✓ or ✗

Addition within 30

Easier adding Name ______ Date ______ B70

8 + 7 + 2 = 17

Find tens if you can.

7 + 5 + 5
2 + 15 + 7
13 + 9 + 1
5 + 7 + 3
8 + 6 + 2
7 + 12 + 3
14 + 3 + 6
11 + 5 + 9
5 + 15 + 5
6 + 8 + 4
9 + 1 + 9
13 + 5 + 8

4 + 2 + 8 + 6 = ____
3 + 1 + 7 + 9 = ____

Addition within 30

Copymasters B69 and B70

Purpose

Encouraging children to think about the strategies they use when adding
Showing that starting with the largest number, or looking for pairs of numbers which make 10, can help make adding easier

Materials

Calculator

Supporting activity

► Work with a partner. Make up sums for each other to do, and do each sum in a different order. Talk about how you worked them out.

Using the textbook pages

Every adult uses a variety of mental methods for addition, depending on the particular sum. These pages should be used to encourage children to talk about the methods they use, and to think about whether they can make sums easier to do by adding in a different order.

Questions 1 to 18 concentrate on starting with the largest number. Questions 19 to 24 use the child's knowledge of bonds to 10 (practised in 'Footballs' on textbook pages 10 and 11) to make adding easier. Make sure that children realise they will not always be able to find a ten, though!

Allow children to try each sum in more than one order if they wish, to compare answers and the time it takes them.

Answers **1** 10 **2** 10 **3** 15 **4** 15 **5** 19 **6** 19 **7** 16 **8** 19 **9** 19 **10** 17 **11** 17 **12** 13 **13** 19 **14** 18 **15** 14 **16** 16 **17** 13 **18** 20 **19** 14 **20** 16 **21** 22 **22** 19 **23** 19 **24** 17

Using the copymasters

Copymaster B69 Addition sums, mostly in a horizontal layout.

Copymaster B70 Addition sums, mostly in a vertical layout.

Textbook 3 pages 14 and 15

Speedy sums

Speedy sums

Work with a friend.

Write question numbers 1 to 20.
Ask your friend to read the questions to you.

Write your answers as quickly as you can.

1 2 + 8
2 0 + 4
3 6 + 3
4 5 + 5
5 2 + 5
6 1 + 9
7 3 + 5
8 7 − 1
9 10 − 4
10 3 − 0
11 6 − 3
12 7 − 4
13 4 − 2
14 9 − 4
15 1 + 5
16 8 − 6
17 4 + 4
18 10 − 3
19 7 + 2
20 9 − 8

✓ or ✗

Now you read the questions to your friend.

14 Mental recall of bonds within 10

Do these all make 10? Write Yes or No.

21 0 + 10
22 2 + 7
23 3 + 7
24 5 + 5
25 8 + 1
26 6 + 4

Do these all make 7? Write Yes or No.

27 3 + 4
28 6 + 2
29 10 − 3
30 9 − 2
31 1 + 6
32 5 + 2
33 8 − 2
34 7 − 0
35 4 + 3

Use a stopwatch or a sand timer.

Can you get 20 sums right in 3 minutes?

Check your answers. ✓ or ✗
Count how many you got right.

Talk to your teacher about what to do next.

Mental recall of bonds within 10 15

Textbook pages 14 and 15

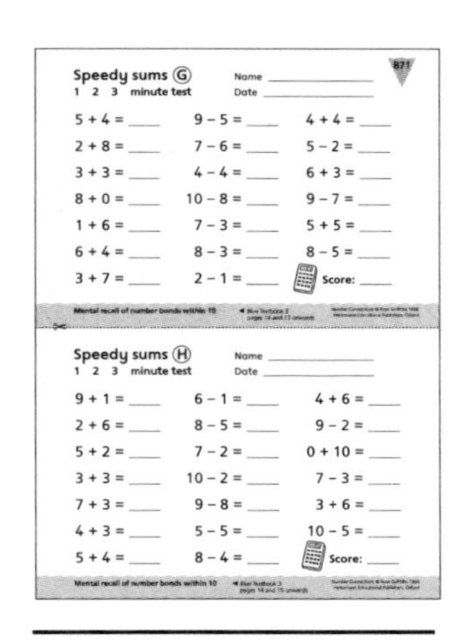

B71

Speedy sums (G) Name ______
1 2 3 minute test Date ______

5 + 4 = ____	9 − 5 = ____	4 + 4 = ____
2 + 8 = ____	7 − 6 = ____	5 − 2 = ____
3 + 3 = ____	4 − 4 = ____	6 + 3 = ____
8 + 0 = ____	10 − 8 = ____	9 − 7 = ____
1 + 6 = ____	7 − 3 = ____	5 + 5 = ____
6 + 4 = ____	8 − 3 = ____	8 − 5 = ____
3 + 7 = ____	2 − 1 = ____	Score: ____

Mental recall of number bonds within 10

Speedy sums (H) Name ______
1 2 3 minute test Date ______

9 + 1 = ____	6 − 1 = ____	4 + 6 = ____
2 + 6 = ____	8 − 5 = ____	9 − 2 = ____
5 + 2 = ____	7 − 2 = ____	0 + 10 = ____
3 + 3 = ____	10 − 2 = ____	7 − 3 = ____
7 + 3 = ____	9 − 8 = ____	3 + 6 = ____
4 + 3 = ____	5 − 5 = ____	10 − 5 = ____
5 + 4 = ____	8 − 4 = ____	Score: ____

Mental recall of number bonds within 10

Copymaster B71

Purpose

Establishing or revising addition and subtraction bonds within 10, and improving immediate mental recall of those number facts

Materials

Stopwatch or 3, 2 and 1 minute sand timers. (Some children may have digital watches with timers on them.)
Calculator

Supporting activity

- ▶ Play the 'Make 9' game, made from Copymasters B60 and B61, and the 'Sums which make 10' game, made from Copymasters B90, B91 and B92.

Using the textbook pages

These pages continue to use a series of timed tests to improve mental recall of addition and subtraction facts. The tests were first introduced in Blue Textbook 1 pages 18 and 19 (for bonds within 8) and continued in Blue Textbook 2 pages 18 and 19 (for bonds within 9). Questions 1 to 20 should be read to the child who is answering them, to help them improve their ability to take in and remember questions without seeing them in print. Some children find it very difficult to listen and concentrate; it can help them if their partner stops for a while after every five questions, to mark them before going on. Marking sums with a calculator helps children remember any they got wrong; it will also remind them that it is quicker to do these smaller sums in your head than on a calculator.

Answers **1** to **20** Marked by child with a calculator **21** Yes **22** No **23** Yes **24** Yes **25** No **26** Yes **27** Yes **28** No **29** Yes **30** Yes **31** Yes **32** Yes **33** No **34** Yes **35** Yes

Using the copymaster

Copymaster B71 This provides two parallel tests covering all the significant bonds within 10. Children should fill in their name and the date first, and *then* time the test. The timing can be done by the teacher; alternatively, two children can take turns in timing each other.

At first, allow children 3 minutes to do as much as they can (and ring the 3 in the top left-hand corner of the test sheet). Repeating the tests, a few days apart, is a very effective way of helping children learn these off by heart, and their scores usually improve quite quickly. When a child has scored 20 on a test, reduce the time you allow them when they next try it to 2 minutes, then finally, if wished, to 1 minute. Children should *always* be trying to beat *their own* previous score, or time – *not* to beat another child. The latter can encourage cheating, and so is not as effective.

Textbook 3 pages 16 and 17

Adding up

Adding up
Use tens and ones.
Fourteen add twelve makes twenty-six.
14
+12
26
Add up the tens and add up the ones.
Use tens and ones. Copy and complete.
1 12 + 17 2 20 + 6 3 13 + 13 4 15 + 14
5 11 + 15 6 23 + 6 7 16 + 10 8 18 + 11

Use tens and ones. Copy and complete.
9 10 + 15 10 15 + 12 11 17 + 11 12 20 + 8
Sometimes when you add up, you will have ten ones.
Swap ten ones for a ten, to make counting easier.
Do this with tens and ones.
15
+ 17
32
Check
Use tens and ones. Copy and complete.
13 16 + 18 14 21 + 15 15 17 + 16 16 20 + 19

Textbook pages 16 and 17

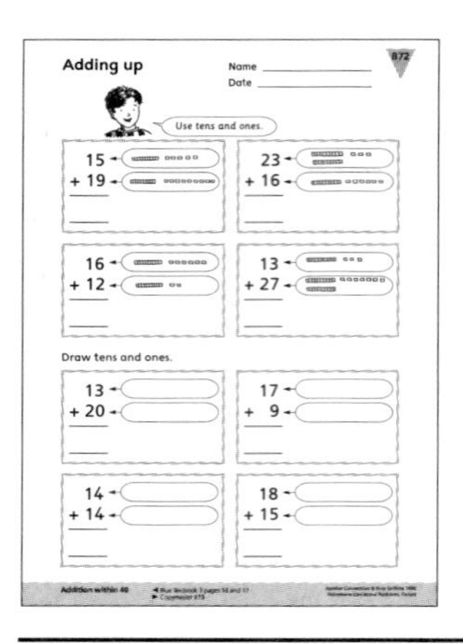
Adding up
Name
Date
Use tens and ones.
15 + 19 23 + 16
16 + 12 13 + 27
Draw tens and ones.
13 + 20 17 + 9
14 + 14 18 + 15

Adding up
Name
Date
Use tens and ones.
25 + 13 19 + 11
16 + 16 17 + 14
Use tens and ones.
15 + 23 30 + 8 17 + 17 21 + 16
20 + 20 14 + 18 7 + 25 18 + 9

Copymasters B72 and B73

Purpose

Making numbers to 40 with base 10 equipment
Using tens and ones to add numbers within 40
Exchanging ten ones for a ten when adding with equipment
Using a vertical layout for addition

Materials

Structured equipment in tens and ones (such as Multibase or Dienes')

Supporting activity

- ▶ Work with a friend. Make up ten sums like the ones on textbook pages 16 and 17 for each other to do with tens and ones.

Using the textbook pages

Using structured equipment was practised in Blue Textbook 2 in 'Teen numbers' on pages 22 and 23 and 'More teen numbers' on pages 26 and 27. Children were introduced to a vertical layout for addition and subtraction. These pages continue to use the vertical layout, and show how you can represent that with tens and ones equipment, including exchanging ten ones for a ten, when appropriate. It is best to have considerable practice at doing this with equipment before suggesting the written method of 'carrying', which will be explained in the Green textbooks.

It is helpful to allow children to choose for themselves whether they work from left to right or right to left when doing these sums. Many successful mathematicians use mental methods of addition which start by adding the tens then adding the units, and children benefit from the opportunity to see that you can get the right answer either way. Starting with the tens makes sense, too, because you immediately get an approximation to the final total. Later on, children can see that it can be easier with pencil and paper methods to start on the right hand side, and add the ones first.

Answers **1** 29 **2** 26 **3** 26 **4** 29 **5** 26 **6** 29 **7** 26 **8** 29 **9** 25 **10** 27 **11** 28 **12** 28 **13** 34 **14** 36 **15** 33 **16** 39

Using the copymasters

Copymasters B72 and B73 It is important that children use the base ten equipment to help them work out the answers to these sums, even if (or perhaps especially if!) they have previously learnt pencil and paper methods for answering these questions.

Drawings of tens and ones equipment are useful not just as a way of showing what children have done, but also as an alternative to using the tens and ones themselves.

Textbook 3 pages 18 and 19

Three times table

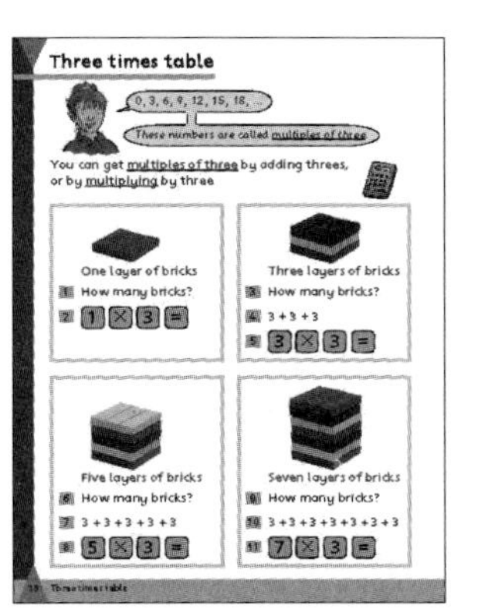
Three times table

0, 3, 6, 9, 12, 15, 18, ...

These numbers are called multiples of three

You can get multiples of three by adding threes, or by multiplying by three

One layer of bricks
1 How many bricks?
2 1 × 3 =

Three layers of bricks
3 How many bricks?
4 3 + 3 + 3
5 3 × 3 =

Five layers of bricks
6 How many bricks?
7 3 + 3 + 3 + 3 + 3
8 5 × 3 =

Seven layers of bricks
9 How many bricks?
10 3 + 3 + 3 + 3 + 3 + 3 + 3
11 7 × 3 =

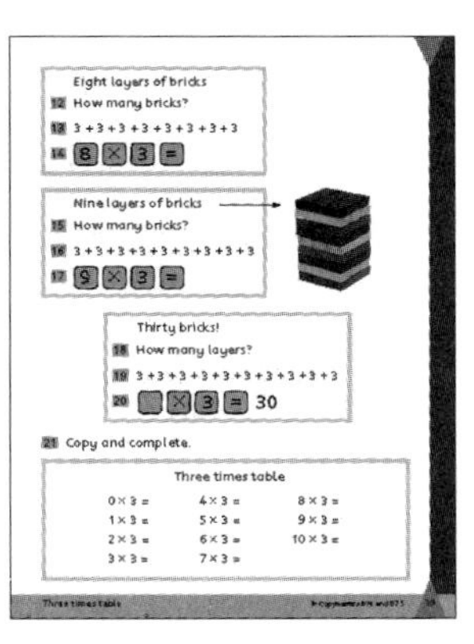
Eight layers of bricks
12 How many bricks?
13 3 + 3 + 3 + 3 + 3 + 3 + 3 + 3
14 8 × 3 =

Nine layers of bricks
15 How many bricks?
16 3 + 3 + 3 + 3 + 3 + 3 + 3 + 3 + 3
17 9 × 3 =

Thirty bricks!
18 How many layers?
19 3 + 3 + 3 + 3 + 3 + 3 + 3 + 3 + 3 + 3
20 × 3 = 30

21 Copy and complete.

Three times table

0 × 3 =	4 × 3 =	8 × 3 =
1 × 3 =	5 × 3 =	9 × 3 =
2 × 3 =	6 × 3 =	10 × 3 =
3 × 3 =	7 × 3 =	

Textbook pages 18 and 19

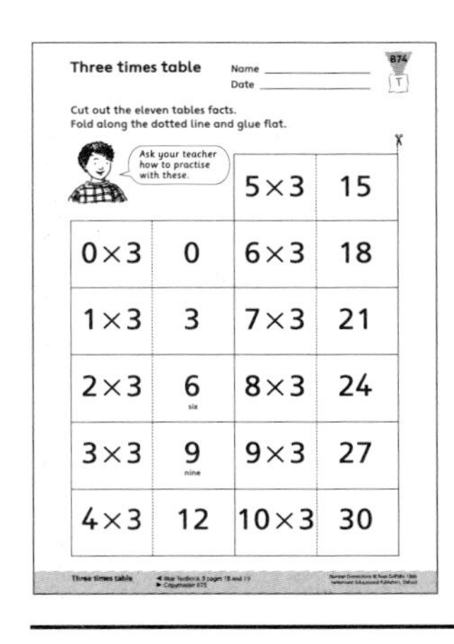
Three times table Name Date B74

Cut out the eleven tables facts. Fold along the dotted line and glue flat.

		5×3	15
0×3	0	6×3	18
1×3	3	7×3	21
2×3	6	8×3	24
3×3	9	9×3	27
4×3	12	10×3	30

Three times table Name Date B75

Fill in the missing numbers. Check with a calculator.

10 × 3 = ☐	10 × 3 = ☐
3 × 10 = ☐	☐ × 3 = 27
4 × 3 = ☐	8 × 3 = ☐
3 × 4 = ☐	7 × 3 = ☐
7 × 3 = ☐	☐ × 3 = 18
3 × 7 = ☐	☐ × 3 = 15
5 × 3 = ☐	4 × 3 = ☐
3 × 5 = ☐	☐ × 3 = 9
	2 × 3 = ☐
	1 × 3 = ☐
	0 × 3 = ☐

Copymasters B74 and B75

Purpose

Establishing and beginning to learn the 3 times table facts
Practising the words 'multiples' and 'multiply'

Materials

Calculator
Scissors and glue (glue stick)
Envelope (to keep tables cards in)

Supporting activities

- Practise counting from 0 to 30 in threes out loud.
- Use the cards made from Copymaster B74 to practise the three times table.

Using the textbook pages

The bricks shown on these pages are part of a game called 'Jenga' or 'Tumbling Tower', where bricks are piled in layers of three, and people take turns to remove a brick at a time, trying not to make the tower fall. Multiples of three up to 18 were practised in Blue Textbook 2 in 'Hopping frogs' on pages 30 and 31.

Questions 1 to 17 emphasise table facts through photographs (on which children can count the bricks), and by adding three over and over again, and lastly by multiplying on a calculator. Children can see that, whichever way you work it out, the answer is the same. Question 18 asks the reverse question (leading to division), 'How many layers?'.

It is important to discuss 0 × 3 = 0. Make sure children agree that if you make no layers of bricks, you will use no bricks.

Answers **1** 3 **2** 3 **3** 9 **4** 9 **5** 9 **6** 15 **7** 15 **8** 15 **9** 21 **10** 21 **11** 21 **12** 24 **13** 24 **14** 24 **15** 27 **16** 27 **17** 27 **18** 10 **19** 30 **20** 10 **21** Child's copy of the 3 times table

Using the copymasters

Copymaster B74 This sheet makes eleven small cards, with a tables question on one side and the answer on the other. Provide each child with an envelope to keep them in. Show children how to practise: shuffle the cards and put them in a pile, questions up. Answer the top question, then turn it over to see if you got it right. If you did, put it to one side; if not, put it at the bottom of the pile to try again. Then use the cards the other way up – look at the answer, and say what the question is. Use the cards as frequently as you wish. Children can work individually, or with a partner, or take them home to practise.

Copymaster B75 Children who feel confident can use this as a test. Those who still need support should use a calculator to check as they go along.

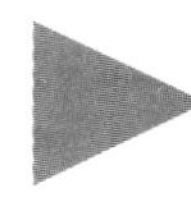

Textbook 3 pages 20 and 21

Fifty pences

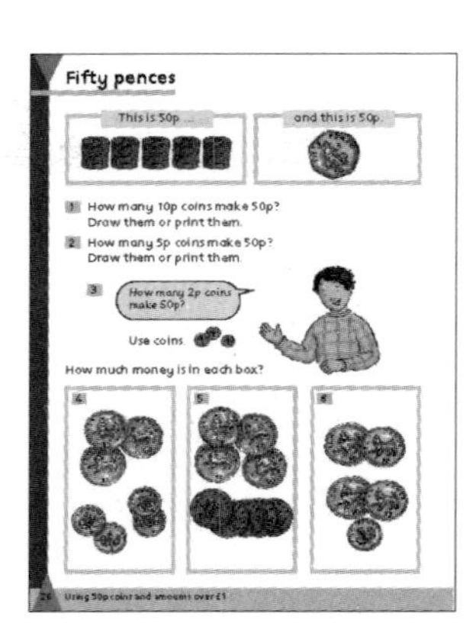

Fifty pences

This is 50p ... and this is 50p.

1 How many 10p coins make 50p? Draw them or print them.

2 How many 5p coins make 50p? Draw them or print them.

3 How many 2p coins make 50p?

Use coins

How much money is in each box?

4 5 6

Using 50p coins and amounts over £1

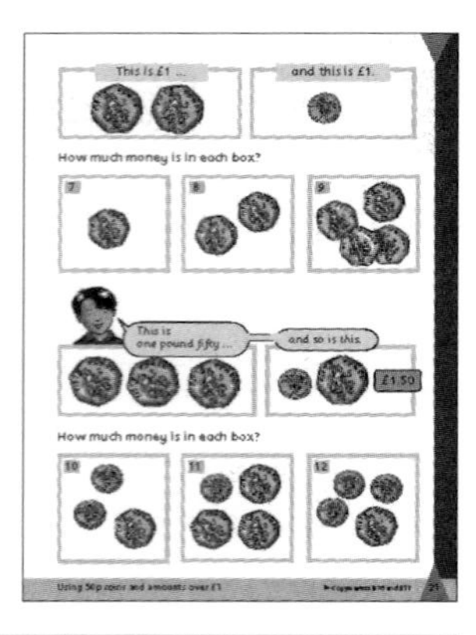

This is £1 ... and this is £1.

How much money is in each box?

7 8 9

This is one pound fifty ... and so is this. £1.50

How much money is in each box?

10 11 12

Textbook pages 20 and 21

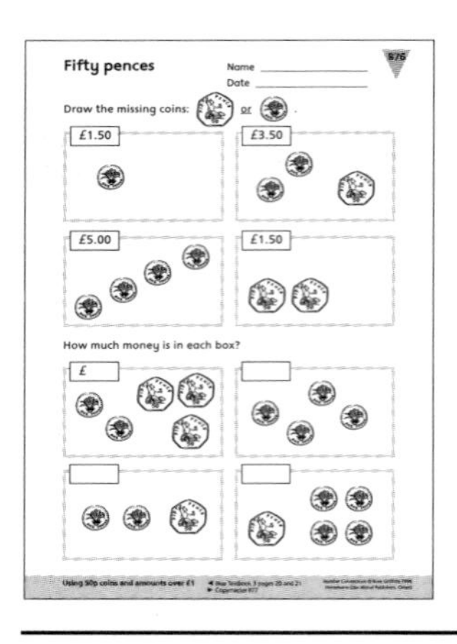

Fifty pences

Name

Date

Draw the missing coins:

£1.50 £3.50

£5.00 £1.50

How much money is in each box?

£

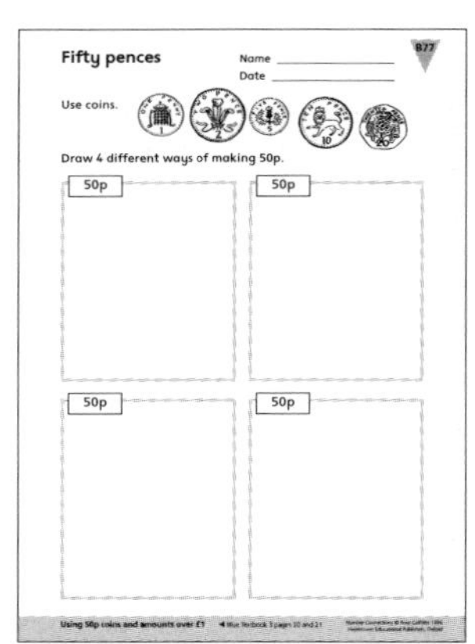

Fifty pences

Name

Date

Use coins.

Draw 4 different ways of making 50p.

50p 50p

50p 50p

Copymasters B76 and B77

Purpose

Finding ways of making 50p using 1p, 2p, 5p, or 10p coins
Counting amounts up to 50p in mixed coins
Writing amounts over £1 using a decimal point
Counting amounts up to £5 using 50p and £1 coins

Materials

Coins (real or token); enough 1p, 2p, 5p and 10p coins to make 50p of each; enough 50p and £1 coins to make £5 of each

Supporting activity

► Work with a friend. Count out an amount of money (but not more than 50p). Your friend has to give you the same amount, but using different coins.

Using the textbook pages

It is helpful to count 50p in 1p coins by putting them in piles of 10p, like the ones in the illustration, before starting these pages.

Questions 1 to 6 use the context of money to revise counting in 1s, 2s, 5s and 10s, and then counting in 10s and 5s or 2s.

Many children are familiar with reading prices written in pounds and pence using a decimal point, but are less confident when they come to writing them down themselves. Make sure they realise that they should never write the pound sign *and* the p for pence on the same price. If they need practice in writing a £ sign properly, use Red Textbook 3 pages 18 and 19 'Pounds', and Copymaster R76.

This work is revised on textbook pages 24 and 25, in 'Swimming'.

Answers **1** 5 **2** 10 **3** 25 **4** 50p **5** 50p **6** 45p **7** 50p **8** £1 **9** £2 **10** £2.50 **11** £2.50 **12** £3.50

Using the copymasters

Copymaster B76 This practises using £1 and 50p coins.

Copymaster B77 Suggest that children ask a friend to check each way they find.

Textbook 3 pages 22 and 23

Dog's toys

Dog's toys

My dog likes squeaky toys.

They are £2 each.

1 How much for 3 toys?

2 3 × 2 =

3 How much for 5 toys?

4 5 × 2 =

5 How much for 8 toys?

6 8 × 2 =

Multiplication and division by 2

I spent £6.

How many toys did she buy?

How many 2s make 6?

6 ÷ 2 = 3

divided by

3 toys!

I spent £8.

7 How many toys?

8 8 ÷ 2 =

I spent £12.

9 How many toys?

10 1 2 ÷ 2 =

Multiplication and division by 2

Textbook pages 22 and 23

Dog's toys Name Date B78

Squeaky toys £2 each

How many toys for £4?

Put the pounds in twos.

4 ÷ 2 = ____

How many toys for £6?

6 ÷ 2 = ____

How many toys for £8?

8 ÷ 2 = ____

How many toys for £10?

10 ÷ 2 = ____

How many toys for £12?

12 ÷ 2 = ____

Multiplication and division by 2

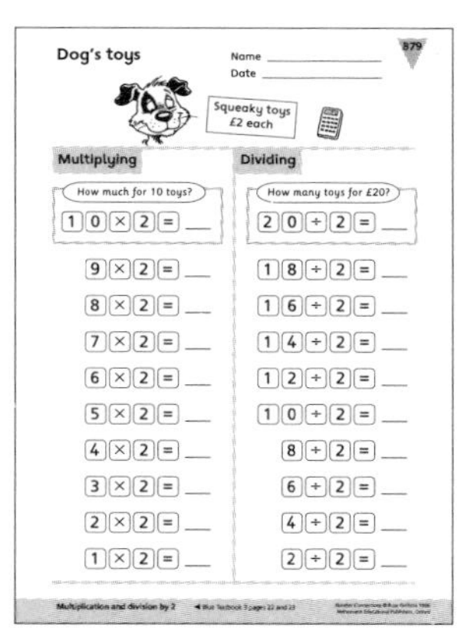
Dog's toys Name Date B79

Squeaky toys £2 each

Multiplying	Dividing
How much for 10 toys?	How many toys for £20?
1 0 × 2 = __	2 0 ÷ 2 = __
9 × 2 = __	1 8 ÷ 2 = __
8 × 2 = __	1 6 ÷ 2 = __
7 × 2 = __	1 4 ÷ 2 = __
6 × 2 = __	1 2 ÷ 2 = __
5 × 2 = __	1 0 ÷ 2 = __
4 × 2 = __	8 ÷ 2 = __
3 × 2 = __	6 ÷ 2 = __
2 × 2 = __	4 ÷ 2 = __
1 × 2 = __	2 ÷ 2 = __

Multiplication and division by 2

Copymasters B78 and B79

Purpose

Looking at division as the inverse (opposite) of multiplication
Introducing using the division sign ÷
Practising multiplication and division facts for the 2 times table

Materials

Calculator
20 '£1 coins' or counters

Supporting activity

- Work with a friend. Take turns in saying how many toys you would buy for dog. Your friend has to say what this would cost if they were £2 each.

Using the textbook pages

Children practised the two times table in Blue Textbook 2 on pages 10 and 11. Questions 1 to 6 revise this.

Make sure children understand and agree with the example at the top of textbook page 23. Children who have already met the division symbol may say it as 'shared by'; this is not appropriate in this context, so make sure children hear and say 'divided by' instead.

Questions 7 and 9 can be answered by trial and improvement (i.e. by guessing, then making the guess bigger or smaller if needed), or by repeated subtraction of £2 to see how many toys could be bought. Questions 8 and 10 use the calculator to demonstrate how to do these problems using the division key.

'Dog food' on textbook pages 26 and 27 provides more practice at multiplying and dividing by 2.

Answers **1** £6 **2** 6 **3** £10 **4** 10 **5** £16 **6** 16 **7** Multiplying and dividing by 2 **8** 4 **9** 6 **10** 6

Using the copymasters

Copymaster B78 The £1 coins are illustrated here so that children can put a ring round each lot of £2, to see how many there are.

Copymaster B79 This sheet lists the 2 times table facts next to the matching division facts, in descending order.

Textbook 3 pages 24 and 25

Swimming

Textbook pages 24 and 25

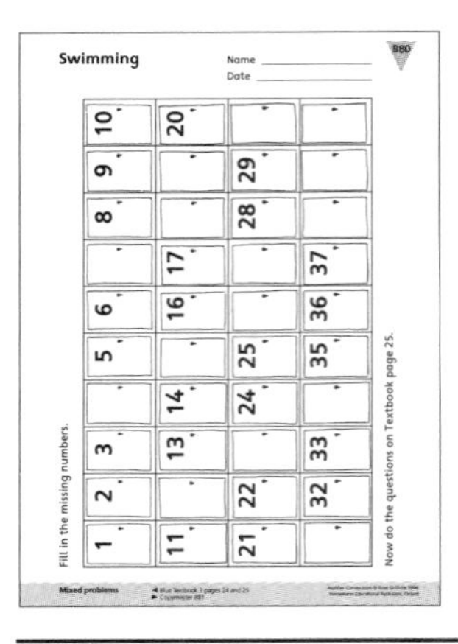

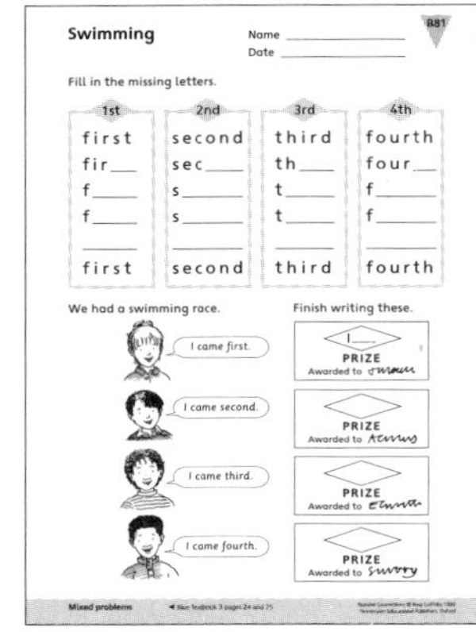

Copymasters B80 and B81

Purpose

Revising the use of 50p and £1 coins, and using decimal notation for money
Using a number grid in rows of 10 for numbers to 40
Spelling and using ordinal numbers, 1st, 2nd, 3rd and 4th

Materials

Token coins: five 50p and five £1 coins (optional: for additional support)

Supporting activity

- Make up some more questions like those on textbook page 24 for a friend to try; ask your friend to make some up for you.

Using the textbook pages

Questions 1 to 8 follow up the work done in 'Fifty pences' on textbook pages 20 and 21. Some children will be able to do these in their heads, or with pencil and paper; some may want to use coins to 'pay' for each person separately, then add up the total.

Copymaster B80 needs to be completed *before* doing questions 9 to 12. When children have finished these questions, it is useful to take turns at making up similar questions to ask each other.

Answers **1** £1 **2** £3 **3** £2.50 **4** £4 **5** £1.50 **6** £2.50 **7** £3.50 **8** £2 **9** 38 **10** 1, 2, 3, 4, 5, 6, 7, 8, 9, or 10 **11** 6, 16, 26, or 36 **12** 4 and 5

Using the copymasters

Copymaster B80 This sheet needs to be done before questions 9 to 12 on textbook page 25. Talk to children about their own visits to swimming pools. Are there lockers like this where they go?

Copymaster B81 This provides straightforward spelling practice, and an opportunity to practise writing the number abbreviations 1st, 2nd, 3rd and 4th, on the prize certificates. This sheet can be repeated if a child needs more practice.

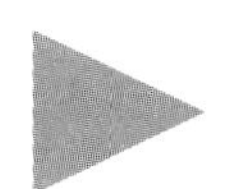

Textbook 3 pages 26 and 27

Dog food

Dog food

Dog food

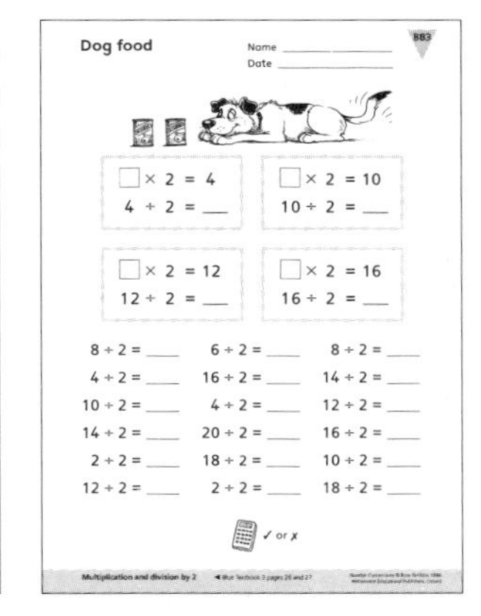

Dog food

Textbook pages 26 and 27

Copymasters B82 and B83

Purpose

Looking at the links between multiplication and division
Using multiplication and division facts from the 2 times table

Materials

Calculator

Supporting activity

- Use the two times table cards made from Copymaster B36 to practise saying the answer to each question, and saying what the question is when you know the answer.

Using the textbook pages

Children practised the two times table in Blue Textbook 2 on pages 10 and 11, and revised it in this book in 'Dog's toys' on pages 22 and 23. These pages use a similar format with a linked context to show that division 'undoes' multiplication.

'Dog's toys' looked at the two times table number facts in order, to help establish the pattern. 'Dog food' uses the facts in random order, and is therefore more difficult. Some children may want to draw the tins of dog food to help them work out their answers to questions 1 to 8; suggest this to any child who seems to need extra help. Make sure that children remember how to check using a calculator, too.

Discuss the example given at the top of textbook page 27, and make sure children can see, from the illustration, that the answer must be 4 days (as well as noticing that the dog has worked it out!). Show children how you can work this out on a calculator, doing $8 \div 2 = 4$. As before, use the phrase 'divided by' out loud as often as possible, so that children become thoroughly familiar with it.

Questions 9 to 14 emphasise the links between multiplication and division.

Answers **1** 8 **2** 12 **3** 4 **4** 14 **5** 10 **6** 16 **7** 18 **8** 20 **9** 5 **10** 5 **11** 5 **12** 7 **13** 7 **14** 7

Using the copymasters

Copymaster B82 Children who are very confident about their two times table could use this sheet as a test. The tables facts are given in random order, and some are repeated in reverse order. The boxes at the bottom of the page give a multiplication fact with an associated division one.

Copymaster B83 This follows a similar pattern to B82, with an emphasis on division.

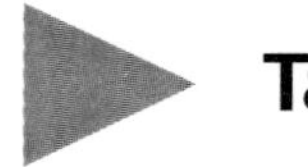

Textbook 3 pages 28 and 29

Taking away

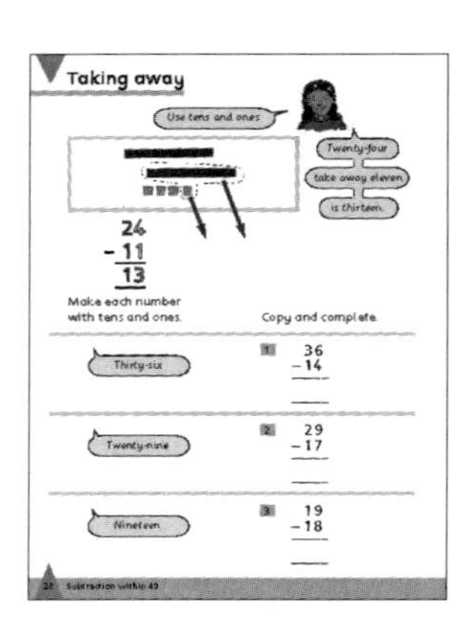

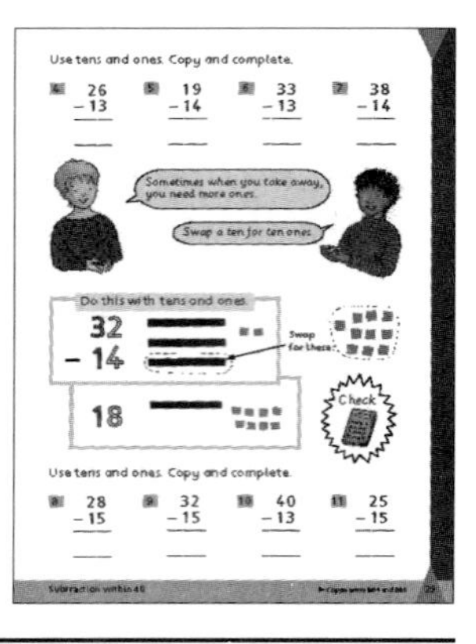

Textbook pages 28 and 29

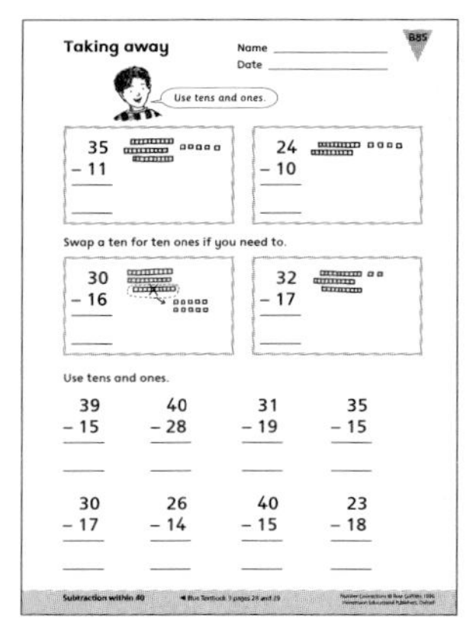

Copymasters B84 and B85

Purpose

Using tens and ones to subtract numbers within 40
Exchanging a ten for ten ones when subtracting with equipment
Using a vertical layout for subtraction

Materials

Structured equipment in tens and ones (such as Multibase or Dienes')

Supporting activity

► Work with a friend. Make up five sums like the ones on textbook pages 28 and 29 for each other to do with tens and ones.

Using the textbook pages

Using structured equipment to carry out additions within 40 was practised earlier in this book, in 'Adding up' on textbook pages 16 and 17. These pages continue to use the vertical layout for subtraction, and show how you can represent that with tens and ones equipment, including exchanging a ten for ten ones, when appropriate. It is best to have considerable practice at doing this with equipment before using the pencil and paper method of 'decomposition', which will be explained in the Green textbooks.

In Blue Textbook 2, in 'More teen numbers' on pages 26 and 27, children were shown two methods of representing what happens when you take away, and these methods are used again here. *Arrows* are used with the photograph on textbook page 28, and *crossing out* on the copymasters.

Children should be expected to use tens and ones when they do these sums. Textbook page 29 includes an example which requires changing a ten for ten ones. It is best to have considerable practice at doing this with equipment before suggesting the written method of 'decomposition', which will be explained in the Green textbooks. Make sure that children realise that they do not always have to change a ten for ten ones!

Answers **1** 22 **2** 12 **3** 1 **4** 13 **5** 5 **6** 20 **7** 24 **8** 13 **9** 17 **10** 27 **11** 10

Using the copymasters

Copymasters B84 and B85 Use tens and ones to show children how the first question on each sheet is done, and to show how the drawing (and crossing out) is used.

Textbook 3 pages 30 and 31

Secret numbers

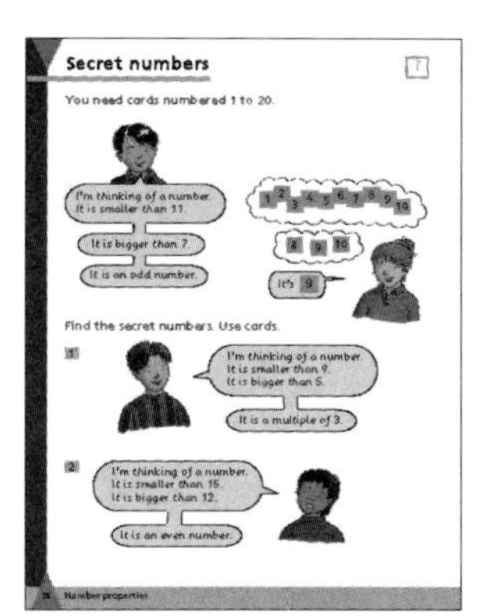

Secret numbers

You need cards numbered 1 to 20.

Find the secret numbers. Use cards.

1. I'm thinking of a number. It is smaller than 9. It is bigger than 5. It is a multiple of 3.
2. I'm thinking of a number. It is smaller than 15. It is bigger than 12. It is an even number.

Number properties

3. I'm thinking of a number. It is bigger than 10. It is smaller than 18. It is a multiple of 5.
4. I'm thinking of a number. It is bigger than 6. It is smaller than 11. It is a multiple of 5.
5. I'm thinking of a number. It is smaller than 17. It is bigger than 7. It is a multiple of 10.
6. I'm thinking of a number. It is smaller than 19. It is bigger than 15. It is a multiple of 3.

Number properties

Textbook pages 30 and 31

Secret numbers Name ____ Date ____ B86

Use cards numbered 1 to 20.

Which numbers belong in each box?

Even numbers 2 4

Odd numbers 1 3

Multiples of 2

Multiples of 3

Multiples of 5

Multiples of 10

Number properties

Secret numbers Name ____ Date ____ B87

Use cards numbered 1 to 20.
Make up puzzles. Give them to a friend.

These puzzles are for ____

Number properties

Copymasters B86 and B87

Purpose

Revising odd and even numbers
Revising multiples of 2, 3, 5 and 10
Checking understanding of 'bigger than' and 'smaller than'
Encouraging logical thinking

Materials

Cards numbered 1 to 20

Supporting activity

► Work with a friend; use cards numbered 1 to 20. You secretly choose a number from 1 to 20, and your friend has to work out what it is. Your friend is only allowed to ask 'Is it bigger than ...?' or 'Is it smaller than ...?'

Using the textbook pages

Like most games, this activity works best if the teacher works through some examples to make sure children understand what to do. Encourage children to work with a friend to do these pages, as discussion is very helpful. It is important to make sure that children know that, for example, 'It is bigger than 8' means that it cannot be 8; similarly, that 'It is smaller than 8' means it could be 1 to 7, but not 8.

As shown in the example on textbook page 30, make sure children use numbered cards to help them solve these puzzles, gradually eliminating cards as they read more clues.

If wished, Copymaster B86 could be completed before children use the textbook pages, and then used as a reference sheet for the puzzles.

Answers **1** 6 **2** 14 **3** 15 **4** 10 **5** 10 **6** 18

Using the copymasters

Copymaster B86 Make sure children realise that the same number can be in several boxes on this sheet, so they need to use the whole pack of 1 to 20 cards each time, to sort through and decide which ones belong in each box.

This sheet can be used as a reference sheet for the textbook pages.

Copymaster B87 It is more difficult to make up successful puzzles than to solve them. It is helpful to use number cards to move aside as the child makes up each successive clue; suggest that the 'bigger than' and 'smaller than' questions should be chosen to leave only 2, 3 or 4 cards still to pick from.

If wished, this sheet can be repeated.

Textbook 3 page 32

Make a dozen

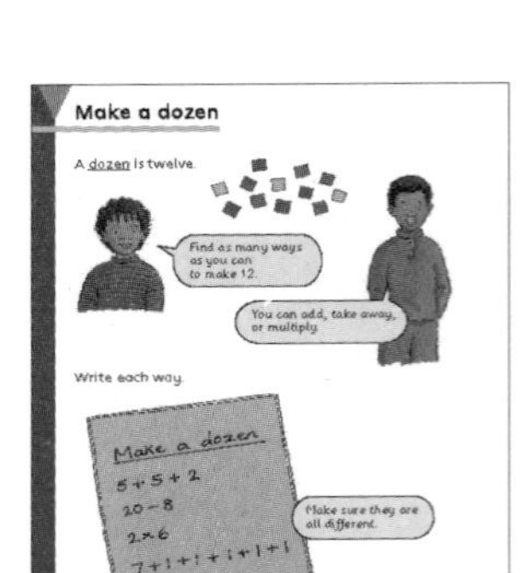

Make a dozen

A dozen is twelve.

Find as many ways as you can to make 12.

You can add, take away, or multiply.

Write each way.

Make a dozen
5 + 5 + 2
20 − 8
2 × 6
7 + 1 + 1 + 1 + 1 + 1

Make sure they are all different.

Ask a friend to check.

✓ or ✗

Combinations to make 12

Textbook page 32

Purpose

Making sure children know what 'dozen' means

Investigating ways of making 12 using addition, subtraction and multiplication

Materials

Calculator

Using the textbook page

Children investigated ways of making 12 by adding two numbers in Blue Textbook 1 in 'More card sums', page 32. This page encourages them to broaden the range of operations they use, to include subtraction and multiplication. There are an infinite number of ways of making 12, so you may want to suggest a time limit – or leave it to the child to decide when to stop.

Most children will approach this in a fairly random manner, but they should be encouraged to check that they have not repeated a way of making 12 as they go along. They may wish to work with a partner, to check that each other's sums do come to 12.

Children can use a calculator both to try out possible sums, and to check ones they have already written down.

Progress tests

The copiable Progress tests on the next six pages can be used in a variety of ways. There are two parallel tests for each textbook, using similar questions but with different numbers. This enables you to give alternative versions to children who are sitting next to each other, when more than one child is ready to try the test at the same time. It also means that you can use one version as a practice or revision exercise, if you wish.

The tests are intended to be used primarily as one way of showing children that they are making progress, and should be given after a child has completed all the work in each textbook. Where a context for a problem is used in a test, it is always one which the child has previously met in the textbook or associated games and copymasters. This reduces the need for help with reading, but it is best to assume that many children will need questions to be read to them, as they go along.

Before children start work, talk to them about how important it is for them to do the best they can *on their own*, so that you and they can find out what things they still need to practice. Explain that although you would usually help them in maths, you would like them to try this sheet completely by themselves (although you *will* help with reading). Most children will feel more confident working in pencil not pen.

If a child is not successful with any part of the test then they should be given the opportunity to revise that area, and play any of the games which practise that concept (see *Games* on page 10). After a period of revision and practice give the child the alternative version of the test to record improvement

The tests give a mark out of ten. The main items tested are:

Tests for Blue Textbook 1

Question 1	Counting to 50
Question 2	Spelling numbers one to ten
Question 3	Counting backwards in ones, within 50
Question 4	Number bonds to 8
Question 5	Addition within 20
Question 6	Multiples of 2
Question 7	Multiples of 10
Question 8	Subtraction within 20
Questions 9 and 10	Multiples of 5

Tests for Blue Textbook 2

Question 1	Counting to 60 in tens and ones
Question 2	Spelling numbers eleven to twenty
Question 3	Representing a number within 60 with tens and ones
Questions 4 and 5	Multiples of 2
Question 6	Multiples of 5
Questions 7 and 8	Addition and subtraction within 20
Question 9	Telling time to half hours
Question 10	Multiples of 3

Tests for Blue Textbook 3

Question 1	Counting to 75 in tens and ones
Question 2	Spelling numbers thirty to seventy five
Question 3	Multiples of 5
Question 4	Number bonds to 10
Question 5	Multiples of 3
Questions 6 and 7	Dividing by 2
Question 8	Using 50p coins and amounts over £1
Questions 9 and 10	Addition and subtraction within 30

Progress test

Blue Textbook 1 Version A

Name ____________________

Date ____________________

1 How many candles? _____

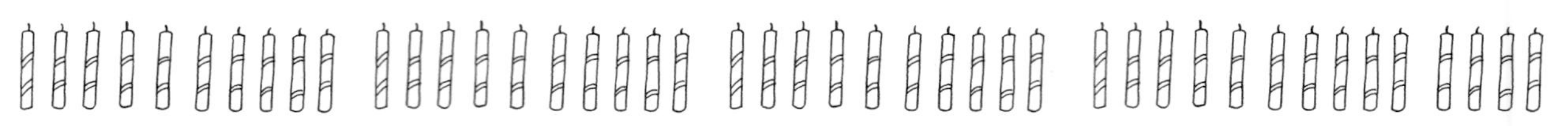

2 Write these numbers as words:

______________ ______________ ______________

Write the missing numbers:

3 34, 33, 32, 31, _____, _____, _____, _____

4 2 + ☐ = 8

5 7 + 9 = _____

6 22, 24, 26, 28, _____, _____, _____, _____.

One spider needs 10 pipecleaners.

7 How many pipecleaners for 5 spiders? _____

8

How much change?

____

---

9 How much money? _______

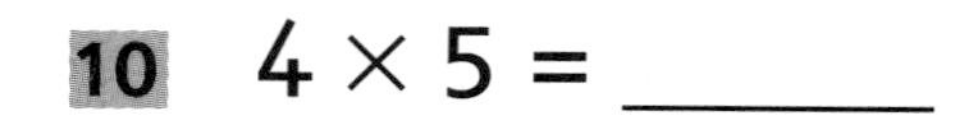

10 $4 \times 5 =$ _______

Progress test

Blue Textbook 1 Version B

Name ____________________

Date ____________________

1 How many paperclips? _____

2 Write these numbers as words:

6   4   2

______________   ______________   ______________

Write the missing numbers:

3 45, 44, 43, 42, _____ , _____ , _____ , _____

4 5 + ☐ = 8

5 9 + 8 = _____

6 18, 20, 22, 24, _____ , _____ , _____ , _____ .

One spider needs 10 pipecleaners.

7 How many pipecleaners for 4 spiders? ______

8

____

---

9 How much money? _______

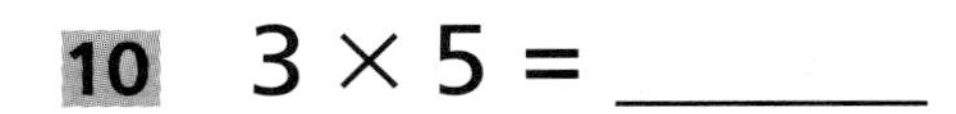

10 $3 \times 5 =$ _______

Progress test

Blue Textbook 2 Version A

Name ______________________

Date ______________________

1 How much money? _____

2 Write these numbers as words:

________________ ________________ ________________

3 This is 24.

Draw 47:

Write the missing numbers:

4 $6 \times 2 = \square$

5 $\square \times 2 = 20$

6 $6 \times 5 = \square$

7
$$\begin{array}{r} 12 \\ +\ 7 \\ \hline \\ \hline \end{array}$$

8
$$\begin{array}{r} 19 \\ -\ 8 \\ \hline \\ \hline \end{array}$$

9

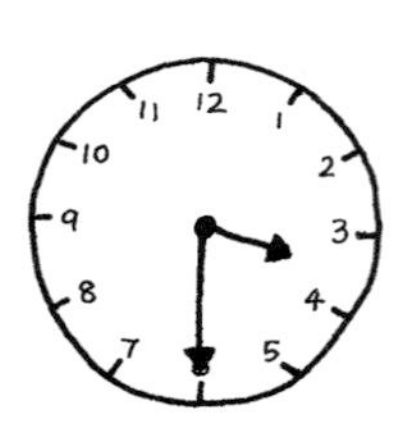

What is the time?

____

10 Score 3 points for each frog.

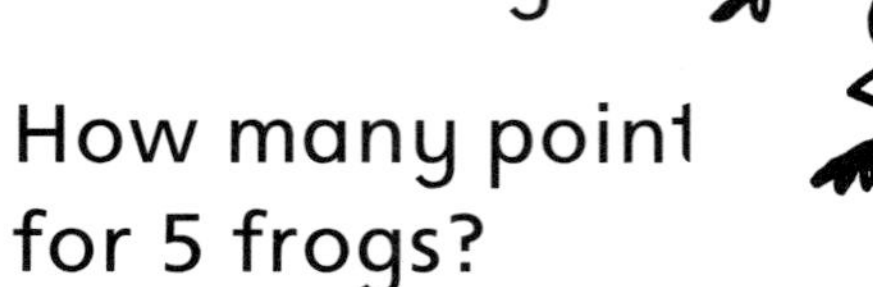

How many point for 5 frogs?

____

Progress test

Blue Textbook 2 Version B

Name ______________________

Date ______________________

1 How much money? ______

2 Write these numbers as words:

________________ ________________ ________________

3 This is 24.

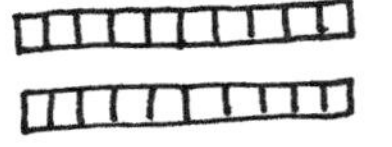

Draw 45:

Write the missing numbers:

4 $7 \times 2 = \square$

5 $\square \times 2 = 12$

6 $4 \times 5 = \square$

7 $13 + 6 =$ ______

8 $18 - 5 =$ ______

9

What is the time?

____

10 Score 3 points for each frog.

How many points for 6 frogs?

____

Progress test

Blue Textbook 3 Version A

Name ____________________

Date ____________________

1 How many ants? _____

2 Write these numbers as words:

______________ ______________ ______________

Write the missing numbers:

3 15, 20, 25, 30, _____, _____, _____, _____

4 $3 + \square = 10$

5 $6 \times 3 =$ _____

6

How many toys for £8?

____

7 $10 \div 2 =$ _____

8 How much money? _____

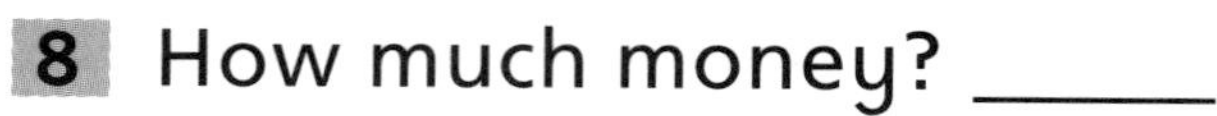

Draw tens and ones to help you.

9

$$\begin{array}{r} 14 \\ +13 \\ \hline \end{array}$$

_____

10

$$\begin{array}{r} 27 \\ -12 \\ \hline \end{array}$$

_____

Progress test

Blue Textbook 3 Version B

Name ______________________

Date ______________________

1 How many spiders? _____

2 Write these numbers as words:

_______________ _______________ _______________

Write the missing numbers:

3 20, 25, 30, 35, _____ , _____ , _____ , _____

4 $6 + \square = 10$

5 $5 \times 3 =$ _____

6

How many toys for £10?

____

7 $8 \div 2 =$ _____

8 How much money? _____

Draw tens and ones to help you.

9

$$\begin{array}{r} 13 \\ +15 \\ \hline \\ \hline \end{array}$$

10

$$\begin{array}{r} 28 \\ -14 \\ \hline \\ \hline \end{array}$$

Record sheet

Pupil's name ______________________________

Blue Textbook 1

Mathematical content

- ▶ Counting to 50
- ▶ Grouping in tens
- ▶ Spelling numbers one to ten
- ▶ Using money (1p, 2p, 5p, £1 and £10)
- ▶ Addition and subtraction within 20
- ▶ Mental recall of number bonds to 8
- ▶ Multiples of 2, 5 and 10 to 50

TEXTBOOK				COPYMASTERS			
Page			*Date completed*	*✓ if used* *✗ if not needed*		*Games (shade if played)*	
4	**Fill the box**	Counting to 50		B1			
6	**More or less**	Counting backwards or forwards		B2	B3		
8	**Spelling numbers**	Spelling one to ten		B4	B5		
10	**Eight bats**	Addition bonds to 8		B6	B7		
12	**Number links**	Links between add^{n} and sub^{n}		B8	B9		
14	**Off by heart**	Mental recall of addition within 8		B10		Sums which make 8	
16	**Spiders and snakes**	Multiples of 2 and 10 to 50		B11	B12		
18	**Speedy sums**	Mental recall of bonds within 8		B13	B14		
20	**T-shirts**	Add^{n} and sub^{n} within 20		B15	B16		
22	**Bowling**	Addition to 10		B17			
24	**Fives and ones**	Counting in 5s to 50		B18	B19		Fifty pence
26	**Pick up bricks**	Grouping in 10s to 50		B20	B21		
28	**Bat and fives**	Multiples of 5 to 50		B22	B23		
30	**Card sums**	Addition within 20		B24	B25		
32	**More card sums**	Addition within 20					

Progress test	*Date completed*	*Score out of 10*
Version A		
Version B		

Other activities

Blue Textbook 1

Record sheet A

Name ____________________

Date started ____________________

Page		**Date completed**	**Copymasters**	
4	Fill the box		B1	
6	More or less		B2	B3
8	Spelling numbers		B4	B5
10	Eight bats		B6	B7
12	Number links		B8	B9
14	Off by heart		B10	
16	Spiders and snakes		B11	B12
18	Speedy sums		B13	B14

Play from page 14 onwards

3 2 4

I played Sums which make 8
on ______________ and ______________

Other activities

Blue Textbook 1

Record sheet B

Name ____________________

Date started ____________________

Page		Date completed	Copymasters	
20	T-shirts		B15	B16
22	Bowling		B17	
24	Fives and ones		B18	B19
26	Pick up bricks		B20	B21
28	Bat and fives		B22	B23
30	Card sums		B24	B25
32	More card sums			

I played Sums which make 8
on ______________ and ______________

Play from page 24 onwards

I played Fifty pence
on ______________ and ______________

Other activities

Progress test Date ____________ Score __________

Record sheet

Pupil's name ______________________________

Blue Textbook 2

Mathematical content

- ▶ Counting to 60
- ▶ Grouping in tens
- ▶ Reading and spelling numbers eleven to twenty
- ▶ Using money (1p, 5p, 10p, £1, £5 and £10)
- ▶ Addition and subtraction within 24 (in 1s) and 50 (in 5s and 10s)
- ▶ Mental recall of number bonds to 9
- ▶ Multiples of 3 to 18, and of 2, 5 and 10 to 50
- ▶ Using $\frac{1}{2}$ (half hours on clock)
- ▶ Ordinal numbers: 1st to 12th

TEXTBOOK				COPYMASTERS				
Page			*Date completed*	*✓ if used* *✗ if not needed*		*Games (shade if played)*		
4	**Coins in a jar**	Counting to 60		B31		Sixty pence		
6	**Sums in words**	Spelling eleven to twenty		B32	B33			
8	**Tens and ones**	Counting in 10s and 1s to 60		B34	B35		Tens & ones	
10	**Two times table**	Two times table		B36	B37			
12	**Hours and half hours**	Using halves; telling the time		B38	B39			
14	**Nine counters**	Addition bonds to 9		B40	B41			Make 9
16	**Fives and tens**	Using 5s and 10s to 50		B42	B43			
18	**Speedy sums**	Mental recall of bonds within 9		B44				
20	**Boxes**	Addition to 20		B45	B46			
22	**Teen numbers**	Addition within 20		B47	B48			
24	**Five times table**	Five times table		B49	B50			
26	**More teen numbers**	Subtraction within 20		B51				
28	**Photos**	Add^{n} and sub^{n} within 24		B52	B53			
30	**Hopping frogs**	Multiples of 3 to 18		B54	B55			
32	**Make £15**	Combinations of 1, 5 and 10 to make 15						

Progress test	*Date completed*	*Score out of 10*
Version A		
Version B		

Other activities

Blue Textbook 2

Record sheet A

Name ______________________

Date started ______________________

Page		Date completed	Copymasters	
4	Coins in a jar		B31	
6	Sums in words		B32	B33
8	Tens and ones		B34	B35
10	Two times table		B36	B37
12	Hours and half hours		B38	B39
14	Nine counters		B40	B41
16	Fives and tens		B42	B43
18	Speedy sums		B44	

Play from page 4 onwards

I played Sixty pence
on ______________ and ______________

Play from page 8 onwards

I played Tens and ones
on ______________ and ______________

Play from page 14 onwards

I played Make 9
on ______________ and ______________

Other activities

Blue Textbook 2

Record sheet B

Name ______________________

Date started ______________________

Page	Date completed	Copymasters	
20 Boxes		B45	B46
22 Teen numbers		B47	B48
24 Five times table		B49	B50
26 More teen numbers		B51	
28 Photos		B52	B53
30 Hopping frogs		B54	B55
32 Make £15			

I played Sixty pence
on ______________ and ______________

I played Tens and ones
on ______________ and ______________

I played Make 9
on ______________ and ______________

Other activities

Progress test Date ____________ Score ________

Record sheet

Pupil's name ______________________

Blue Textbook 2

Mathematical content

- Counting to 75
- Reading and spelling thirty to seventy five
- Using money (1p, 2p, 5p, 10p, 20p, 50p, £1)
- Addition and subtraction within 40
- Mental recall of number bonds to 10
- Multiples of 3 to 30; 2 and 5 to 50; 10 to 70
- Division (including symbol ÷)

TEXTBOOK				COPYMASTERS			
Page			*Date completed*	✓ *if used* ✗ *if not needed*		*Games (shade if played)*	
4	**Joke shop**	Counting to 75		B62			
6	**Tens and teens**	Spelling thirty to seventy		B63	B64	Tens and teens bingo	
8	**What comes next?**	Multiples of 2, 5 and 10		B65	B66		
10	**Footballs**	Add^n and sub^n bonds to 10		B67	B68		Sums which make 10
12	**Easier adding**	Addition within 30		B69	B70		
14	**Speedy sums**	Mental recall of bonds within 10		B71			
16	**Adding up**	Addition within 40		B72	B73		
18	**Three times table**	Three times table		B74	B75		
20	**Fifty pences**	Using 50p coins and amounts over £1		B76	B77		
22	**Dog's toys**	Multiplication and division by 2		B78	B79		
24	**Swimming**	Mixed problems		B80	B81		
26	**Dog food**	Multiplication and division by 2		B82	B83		
28	**Taking away**	Subtraction within 40		B84	B85		
30	**Secret numbers**	Number properties		B86	B87		
32	**Make a dozen**	Combinations to make 12					

Progress test	*Date completed*	*Score out of 10*
Version A		
Version B		

Other activities

Blue Textbook 3

Record sheet A

Name ______________________

Date started ______________________

Page		Date completed	Copymasters	
4	Joke shop		B62	
6	Tens and teens		B63	B64
8	What comes next?		B65	B66
10	Footballs		B67	B68
12	Easier adding		B69	B70
14	Speedy sums		B71	
16	Adding up		B72	B73
18	Three times table		B74	B75

Play from page 6 onwards

I played Tens and teens bingo
on ______________ and ______________

Play from page 10 onwards

I played Sums which make 10
on ______________ and ______________

Other activities

Blue Textbook 3

Record sheet B

Name ______________________

Date started ______________________

Page		Date completed	Copymasters	
20	Fifty pences		B76	B77
22	Dog's toys		B78	B79
24	Swimming		B80	B81
26	Dog food		B82	B83
28	Taking away		B84	B85
30	Secret numbers		B86	B87
32	Make a dozen			

I played Tens and teens bingo
on ______________ and ______________

I played Sums which make 10
on ______________ and ______________

Other activities

Progress test Date ______________ Score ___________

Curriculum coverage charts: Blue level

National Curriculum Key Stage 2 Programme of Study

Using and Applying Mathematics

'Using and Applying Mathematics' is integrated throughout *Number Connections*; every aspect of the programme of study is included.

Number		*Textbook 1*	*Textbook 2*	*Textbook 3*
1 Opportunities to:				
develop flexible and effective methods	a	■	■	■
use calculators	b	■	■	■
develop skills for use of equipment	c	■	■	■
2 Developing an understanding of place value and extending the number system	a	■	■	■
	b			■
	c		■	
3 Understanding relationships between numbers and developing methods of computation	a	■	■	■
	b			
	c	■	■	■
	d	■	■	■
	e	■	■	■
	f			■
	g			
	h	■	■	■
4 Solving numerical problems	a	■	■	■
	b	■	■	■
	c	■	■	■

● Level 1 ■ Level 2

Mathematics 5 to 14 (Number, Money and Measurement)

Strand	*Textbook 1*	*Textbook 2*	*Textbook 3*
Range and type of numbers	■	■	■
Money	■	■	■
Add and subtract	■	■	■
Multiply and divide	■	■	■
Round numbers			
Fractions, percentages and ratio			
Patterns and sequences	■	■	■
Functions and equations	■	■	■

● Level A ■ Level B

Northern Ireland Curriculum Key Stage 2 Programme of Study

Processes in Mathematics

'Processes in Mathematics' is integrated throughout *Number Connections*; every aspect of the programme of study relating to this attainment target is included.

Number		*Textbook 1*	*Textbook 2*	*Textbook 3*
Understanding number and number notation	a	■	■	■
	b			■
	c	■	■	■
	d		■	
Patterns, relationships and sequences	a	■	■	■
	b	■	■	■
	c			
	d			
Operations and their application	a	■	■	■
	b	■	■	■
Money	a	■	■	■
	b			■
	c			■

● Level 1 ■ Level 2